FOOD SCIENCE AND TECHNOLOGY

FOOD SCIENCE RESEARCH BIOGRAPHICAL SKETCHES AND RESEARCH SUMMARIES

VOLUME 1

FOOD SCIENCE AND TECHNOLOGY

Additional books in this series can be found on Nova's website
under the Series tab.

Additional e-books in this series can be found on Nova's website
under the e-book tab.

FOOD SCIENCE AND TECHNOLOGY

FOOD SCIENCE RESEARCH BIOGRAPHICAL SKETCHES AND RESEARCH SUMMARIES

VOLUME 1

LUCILLE MONACO CACIOPPO
EDITOR

nova publishers
New York

For permission to use material from this book please contact us:
Telephone 631-231-7269; Fax 631-231-8175
Web Site: http://www.novapublishers.com

NOTICE TO THE READER

Library of Congress Cataloging-in-Publication Data

ISBN: 978-1-63117-932-7

Published by Nova Science Publishers, Inc. † New York

CONTENTS

PREFACE

This new book compiles biographical sketches of top professionals in the field of food sciences, as well as research summaries from a number of different focuses in this important field.

PART I

BIOGRAPHICAL SKETCHES

In: Food Science Research ... Volume 1
Editor: Lucille Monaco Cacioppo

ISBN: 978-1-63117-932-7
© 2014 Nova Science Publishers, Inc.

Chapter 1

RISHIPAL R. BANSODE

Affiliation: North Carolina Agricultural and Technical State University

Date of Birth: August 12th, 1977

Education: Ph. D. (Food Science)

Research and Professional Experience:

My area of expertise is in lipid metabolism and bioactive compound validation in the area of cancer biology, obesity and diabetes. I have experience in *in vivo* assessment of molecular biochemistry using rodent and zebrafish model systems.

Professional Appointments:

2010 – Curr.	Research Associate, North Carolina A&T State University, Center for Post Harvest Technologies, North Carolina Research Campus, Kannapolis, NC, 28081, USA
2006 – 2010	Postdoctoral Researcher, The Ohio State University, Department of Molecular and Cellular Biochemistry, College of Medicine, Columbus OH 43210 USA
1998 – 2000	Quality Control Officer, Bambino Agro Industries, Hyderabad, India.

Honors:

2009	The JBC 2008 article was included in the JBC annual meeting compendium have been selected from the most cited and read papers published in the *JBC* in 2007-08 (http://www.jbc.org/site/meeting2009/metabolism/

Publications Last 3 Years:

1. Bansode, R.R., Randolph, P., Ahmedna, M., Hurley, S., Hanner, T., Baxter, S., Johnston, T., Su, M., Holmes, B., Yu, J., Williams, L.L. Bioavailability of polyphenols from peanut skin extract associated with plasma lipid lowering function. *Food Chem.* 148(1): 24-29.
2. Bansode, R.R., Leung, T., Randolph, P., Williams, L.L., and Ahmedna. M. (2012) Cinnamon extract inhibits angiogenesis in zebrafish and human endothelial cells by suppressing VEGFR1, VEGFR2 and PKC-mediated MAP kinase. *Food Sci. Nutr.* 1(1): 74-82.
3. Bansode, R. R., Randolph, R., Hurley, S., and Ahmedna, M. (2012). Evaluation of hypolipidemic effects of peanut skin-derived polyphenols in rats on Western-diet. *Food Chem.* 135(3): 1659-66.
4. Huang W, Bansode RR, Bal NC, Mehta M, Mehta KD. (2012) Protein kinase $C\beta$ deficiency attenuates obesity syndrome of ob/ob mice by promoting white adipose tissue remodeling. *J Lipid Res.* 53(3):368-78.
5. Bansode, R.R. Ahmedna, M., Svoboda, K. R., Losso, J.N. (2011) Coupling in vitro and in vivo paradigm reveals a dose-dependent inhibition of angiogenesis followed by inhibition of autophagy by C6-Ceramide. *Int J Biol Sci.* 7(5):629-44.
6. Huang W, Bansode R.R., Xie Y., Rowland L, Mehta M., Davidson N. O. and Mehta K. D. (2011) "Disruption of the protein kinase Cbeta alters biliary lipid and hepatic cholesterol metabolism" *J. Biol. Chem.* 286(26):22795-805.

In: Food Science Research ... Volume 1
Editor: Lucille Monaco Cacioppo

ISBN: 978-1-63117-932-7
© 2014 Nova Science Publishers, Inc.

Chapter 2

GUILHERME WOLFF BUENO

Affiliation: Department of Animal Science, University of Brasília

Date of Birth: 06 January 1984

Education:

2014 – Ph.D. in Animal Science in the University of Guelph, Ontario, Canada
and University of Brasilia
2013 - MBA in Project Management by College FGF,
Brazil
2012 - Masters in Fishery Resources in the State University of West Paraná,
Brazil
2008 - Graduation in Animal Science in the State University of West Paraná,
Brazil

Research and Professional Experience:

Author of two books and eight technical handbooks on aquaculture production system.
15 published articles in peer reviewed international journals including *Reviews in Aquaculture, Aquaculture Research* and *Applied Aquaculture.*
60 oral and poster presentations in national and international scientific symposiums.
Invited reviewer for national and international journal including: *Aquaculture Research, International Journal of Physical Sciences, Journal of the Brazilian Society of Animal Science* and *Brazilian Journal of Agroecology.*

Professional Appointments:

Current coordination and collaboration in projects of fish nutrition and carrying capacity of fish farms in the Brazilian Agricultural Research Corporation, the National Research Council (CNPq) and the Ministry of Fisheries and Aquaculture in Brazil.

Works on projects and studies analyzing the aquaculture production chain, implementation of projects for the production of fish and promotion of sustainable production systems for fish farming in South America and Africa.

Publications Last 3 Years:

Articles in peer reviewed

MATOS, F.T.; LAPOLLI, F.R.; MOHEDANO, R.A.; FRACALOSSI, D.M.; BUENO, G.W.; ROUBACH, R. (2014) Duckweed Bioconversion and Fish Production in Treated Domestic Wastewater. *Journal of Applied Aquaculture*, 26:49–59, 2014. (DOI:10.1080/10454438.2014.877740)

BUENO, G. W.; LEMAINSKI, D.; ROUBACH, R.; MATOS, F.T.; AZEVEDO, D.B.; MATTOS, B.O. Economic Insertion Of Small-Scale Aquaculture In Brazilian Federal Waters: An Analysis Towards The Sustainable Development. (2014) *Journal of Environment and Agribusiness.* v. 7, n. 2, 2014.

BUENO, G. W.; OSTRENSKY, A.; CANZI, C.; MATOS, F.T.; ROUBACH, R. Implementation of aquaculture parks in Federal Government waters in Brazil. (2013) *Reviews in Aquaculture*, v. 5, p. 1–12. 2013. (DOI: 10.1111/raq.12045)

NEU, D.H.; FURUYA, W. M.; BOSCOLO, W. R.; BUENO, G.W.; POTRICH, F. R.; FEIDEN, A. Digestible energy from different sources glycerol for Nile tilapia (*Oreochromis niloticus*). (2012) *Journal Agrária* (Recife. Online), v. 7, p. 174-179, 2012. (DOI:10.5039/agraria.v7i1a1501)

BUENO, G.W.; FEIDEN, A.; NEU, D.H.; WÄCHTER, N.; LUI, T. A.; BOSCOLO, W. R. (2012) Phosphorus digestibility in diets as a nutritional strategy to reduce waste from tilapia. *Brazilian Archives of Veterinary Medicine and Animal Science* (Online), v. 64, p.183-191, 2012. (DOI: 10.1590/S0102-09352012000100026)

SILVA, J.R.; RABENSCHLAG, D. R.; SIGNOR, A.A.; BOSCOLO, W. R.; FEIDEN, A.; BUENO, G.W. (2012) Pacu (*Piaractus mesopotamicus*) economic return from cage production in Itaipu reservoir, Brazil. *Archivos de Zootecnia*, v. 61, p. 245-254, 2012. (DOI: 10.4321/S0004-05922012000200009)

BUENO, G.W.; MATOS, F. T.; CANZI, C.; SAMPAIO, M.B.; BARONE, R.S.C.; ROUBACH, R. (2011) The Carrying Capacity: Production of Fish in Reservoirs. *Panorama da Aquicultura*, v. 21, p. 48-63, 2011.

BUENO, G.W.; MATOS, F. T.; CANZI, C.; SAMPAIO, M.B.; BARONE, R.S.C.; ROUBACH, R. (2011) The Carrying Capacity and Production of Fish in Reservoirs: Tools Used. *Panorama da Aquicultura*, v. 21, p. 45-59, 2011.

National and International Scientific Symposiums

BUENO, G.W.; SKIPPER-HORTON, J.O. AND D.P. BUREAU. *Improving Efficiency of Trout Production in Ontario: Extending this Work to Nile Tilapia in Brazil.* Martin Mills Cage Growers Meeting, 22 March 2014, Midland, Ontario.

ROUBACH, R.; BUENO, G.W. Policies and development strategy of Brazilian aquaculture. *In:* 50th Annual Meeting of the Brazilian Society of Animal Science, Campinas, SP, Brazil, July 22-26, 2013.

BUENO, G.W.; LEMAINSKI, D.; ROUBACH, R.; AZEVEDO, D.B. Aquaculture family in public waters: a look on sustainable development of the production chain of fish. *In:* Congress *of the Brazilian Society of Economics, Business and Rural Sociology – SOBER, 2013, Belém – Brazil.*

AZEVEDO, D.B.; BUENO, G.W.; ORTH, D.; FACHINETTO, J.D.; SILVA, V.G. Integration of dairy cattle farm with the family: an alternative to sustainability. *In:* Congress *of the Brazilian Society of Economics, Business and Rural Sociology – SOBER, 2013, Belém – Brazil.*

SEIDE, M.F.; BARONE, R.S.C.; BUENO, G.W.; LEMAINSKI, D.; MATTOS, B.O.; TAVARES, F.A.; DIETERICH, T.G.; ROUBACH, R.; SAMPAIO, M.B.; MATIAS, J.F.N. Methodology used by the Brazilian ministry of fisheries and aquaculture for estimates of carrying capacity in aquaculture parkrs. *In:* World Aquaculture - WAS, 2011, Recife - Brazil.

MATTOS, B.O.; ANTONELLO, A.; DIETERICH, T.G.; TAVARES, F.A.; SEIDE, M. F.; BARONE, R.S.C.; BUENO, G.W.; LEMAINSKI, D.; ROUBACH, R.; SAMPAIO, M.B.; MATIAS, J.F.N. Aquaculture parks delimitation in federal reservoirs: Zootechinical and socioeconomic evaluation. In: World Aquaculture - WAS, 2011, Recife - Brazil. Aquaculture parks delimitation in federal reservoirs: Zootechinical and socioeconomic evaluation, 2011.

LEMAINSKI, D.; MATTOS, B.O.; BARONE, R.S.C.; BUENO, G.W.; ANTONELLO, A.; SEIDE, M.F.; TAVARES, F.A.; ROUBACH, R.; SAMPAIO, M.B.; MATIAS, J.F.N. Demonstration units as tools for federal waters aquaculture development. In: World Aquaculture - WAS, 2011, Recife - Brazil. Demonstration units as tools for federal waters aquaculture development, 2011.

TAVARES, F.A.; BUENO, G.W.; SEIDE, M.F.; ANTONELLO, A.; DIETERICH, T.G.; LEMAINSKI, D.; MATTOS, B.O.; BARONE, R.S.C.; ROUBACH, R.; SAMPAIO, M.B.; MATIAS, J.F.N. Aquaculture development in brazilian fereral waters. In: World Aquaculture - WAS, 2011, Recife - Brazil. Aquaculture development in brazilian fereral waters, 2011.

Technical Handbooks

BERNAL, F.E.M; ROUBACH, R.; MATTOS, B.O.; MATOS; F.T.; CARVALHO, G.C.; BUENO, G.W. (2013) *Welfare in fish production.* Brazilian National Institute of Science and Technology/INCT Livestock, 5p. 2013 (Technical Series)

In: Food Science Research ... Volume 1
Editor: Lucille Monaco Cacioppo

ISBN: 978-1-63117-932-7
© 2014 Nova Science Publishers, Inc.

Chapter 3

RISHI R. BURLAKOTI

Affiliation: Research Lead and Plant Pathologist, Weather INnovations

Contact Point: 7159 Queens Line RR5, Chatham, ON Canada N7M 5J5

Education: PhD in Plant Pathology

Research and Professional Experience:

2010 to Present: Research Leader, Weather INnovations Incorporated, Chatham, ON.
2011 to Present: Adjunct Professor, Plant Agriculture, University of Guelph
2009-2010: Post-Doctoral Research Fellow, Nova Scotia Agricultural College, NS, Canada.
2008-2009: Post-Doctoral Research Fellow, North Dakota State University, Fargo, ND, USA.
2005-2008: Ph.D. Graduate Research Assistant, North Dakota State University, Fargo, USA
2003-2004: Research Scientist, CIMMYT/Nepal Agriculture Research Council, Nepal

Professional Appointments:

2011 to Present: Adjunct Professor, Plant Agriculture, University of Guelph
2009 to Present: Coordinator, International Development project, Agricultural Institute of Canada

Publications Last 3 Years:

1. Burlakoti, R. R., Shrestha, S. M., and Sharma, R. C. 2013. Effect of natural seed-borne inoculum of *Bipolaris sorokiniana* on the seedling emergence and vigor, and early establishment of foliar blight in pring wheat. Archives of Phytopathology and Plant Protection. DOI:10.1080/03235408.2013.823272.
2. Burlakoti, R. R., Shrestha, S. M., Sharma, R.C.2013. Impact of seed-borne inoculum, irrigation, and cropping pattern on propagation of *Bipolaris sorokiniana* and

epidemiology of foliar blight and common root rot in spring wheat. Journal of Plant Pathology 95:571-578.

3. Burlakoti, R. R., Zandstra, J., Jackson, K., and Fisher, P. 2013. Evaluation of epidemics of gray mold, anthracnose rot and powdery mildew in day-neutral strawberry in Ontario. International Journal of Fruit Science 13:19-27.

4. Burlakoti, R. R., Lynch, D., Halde, C., Beach, T., Dahal, S., and Debnath, S. C. 2012. Organic Agriculture project in Nepal: An international twinning partnership program. Canadian Journal of Plant Science. 92:997-1003.

5. Gyawali, S., Neate, S. M., Adhikari, T. B., Puri, K. D., Burlakoti R. R., and Zhong, S. 2012. Genetic structure of *Cochliobolus sativus* populations sampled from roots and leaves of barley and wheat in North Dakota. Journal of Phytopathology 160:637-646.

6. Burlakoti, R. R., Neate, S. M., Adhikari, T. B., Gyawali, S., Salas, B., and Steffenson, B. J. 2011. Trichothecene Profiling and Population Genetic Analysis of *Gibberella zeae* from Barley in North Dakota and Minnesota. Phytopathology 101:687-695.

In: Food Science Research ... Volume 1
Editor: Lucille Monaco Cacioppo

ISBN: 978-1-63117-932-7
© 2014 Nova Science Publishers, Inc.

Chapter 4

MARIA JOAO CABRITA

Affiliation: ICAAM, Évora University

Contact Point: Laboratorio de Enologia, Nucleo da Mitra, Universidade de Évora, Ap 94 7002-554 Évora

Date of Birth: 26 February, 1966

Education: Ph.D.

Research and Professional Experience: Assistant professor at Évora University and researcher at ICAAM

Professional Appointments: Mainly dedicated to a masters in Oenology and Viticulture at Évora University

Publications Last 3 Years:

A. M. Costa Freitas; M. D. R. Gomes da Silva; M. J. Cabrita (2012) "Sampling and sample preparation techniques for the determination of volatile components in grape juice, wine and alcoholic beverages" In Comprehensive Sampling and Sample Preparation. Volume 4, Pawliszyn J., Mondello L., Dugo P. Eds; Elsevier, Academic Press: Oxford, UK, pp 27–41, 2012. ISBN: 9780123813732; doi:10.1016/B978-0-12-381373-2.10126-7

Marco Gomes Da Silva, Ana Maria Costa Freitas, Maria João Bastos Cabrita and Raquel Garcia. (2012) "Olive oil composition: volatiles compound" pp17- 46 In Olive Oil - Constituents, Quality, Health Properties and Bioconversions, p 510, ISBN 978-953-307-921-9 Edited by Prof. Boskou Dimitrios; Publisher Intech, Publication date: February 2012, Subject: Life Sciences - DOI: 10.5772/28512; http://www.intechopen.com/articles/show/title/oil-composition-volatiles

Maria João Bastos Cabrita, Raquel Garcia, Nuno Martins, Marco Gomes Da Silva and Ana Maria Costa Freitas (2012) "Gas chromatography in analysis of compounds released from wood into wine" pp 185-298 InAdvanced Gas Chromatography - Progress in Agricultural, Biomedical and Industrial Applications, p 460 ISBN 978-953-51-0298-4 Edited by Prof. Mustafa Ali Mohd; Publisher Intech, Publication date: March 2012, Subject: Analytical Chemistry - DOI: 10.5772/32659
http://www.intechopen.com/articles/show/title/gas-chromatography-in-analysis-of-compounds-released-from-wood-into-wine

Mª. Pietra Torres, M.J. Cabrita, M. D. R. Gomes da Silva, V. Palma, and A. Mª. Costa Freitas.The Impact of the Malolactic Fermentation in the Volatile Composition of Trincadeira Wine Variety. *Journal of Food Biochemistry* 35, 3, 898-913 (2011)
http://dx.doi.org/10.1111/j.1745-4514.2010.00424

Vaz Freire, Luis; Cabrita, Maria João; Gomes da Silva, Marco; Freitas, Ana Maria. Sensorial analysis and electronic aroma detection to compare olive oils produced by different extraction methods. *Grasas e Azeites*. 62, 4, 428-435(2011)
http://dx.doi.org/10.3989/gya.010411

M. J. Cabrita; C. Barrocas Dias; A. M. Costa Freitas Phenolic Acids, Phenolic Aldehydes And Furanic Derivatives In Oak Chips: American Vs French Oaks. *South African Journal of Enology And Viticulture*, 32, 2, 204 - 210(2011).

Raquel Garcia, Maria João Cabrita, Ana Maria Costa Freitas. Application of Molecularly Imprinted Polymers for the analysis of pesticide residues in food- a highly selective and innovative approach *American Journal of Analytical Chemistry* 2, 16-25 (2011)
http://dx.doi.org/10.4236/ajac.2011.228119

Mª. J. Cabrita; V. Palma; R. Patão; A. Mª. Costa Freitas The conversion of hydroxycinnamic acids into volatile phenols (in a synthetic media and in red wine) by *Dekkera bruxellensis*. *Revista de Ciência e Tecnologia dos Alimentos*, 32, 1, 1-6 (2012)

Cabrita, Maria João; J.M. Aires de Sousa; Gomes da Silva, Marco; Rei, F., Freitas, Ana Maria. Multivariate statistical approaches for wine classification based on low molecular weight phenolic compounds. *Australian Journal of Grape and Wine Research*.18, 138-146 (2012) doi: 10.1111/j.1755-0238.2012.00182.x

Raquel Garcia, Bruno Soares, Cristina Barrocas Dias, Ana Maria Costa Freitas, Maria João Cabrita. Phenolic and Furanic Compounds of Portuguese Chestnut and French, American and Portuguese Oak Wood Chips. *European Food Research and Technology* 235, 457-467 (2012) DOI: 10.1007/s00217-012-1771-2

Bruno Soares; Raquel Garcia; Ana Maria Costa Freitas; Maria João Cabrita. Phenolic compounds released from oak, cherry, chestnut and robinia chips into a syntethic wine: influence of toasting level. *Ciência e Técnica Vitivinicola / Journal of Viticulture and Enology*. 27 (1): 17-26 (2012)

Nuno Martins; Raquel Garcia; Marco Gomes Da Silva; Maria João Cabrita. Volatiles compounds from oak, cherry, chestnut and acacia chips: influence of toasting level. *Ciência e Técnica Vitivinicola / Journal of Viticulture and Enology*. 27 (1): 49-57 (2012)

Palma V., Agulheiro-Santos A.C., Machado G., Rato A.E., Cabrita M.J., Lozano M. and Gónzález D. Effect of different storage conditions on nutritional and quality parameters of 'sweetheart' cherry. *Acta Hort*. (ISHS) 934:1027-1032 (2012)
http://www.actahort.org/books/934/934_137.htm

Agulheiro-Santos A.C., Palma V., Machado G., Rato A.E. and Cabrita M.J. quality evaluation of 'sunburst' cherries harvested at different ripeness stages. *Acta Hort.* (ISHS) 934:1127-1131 (2012) http://www.actahort.org/books/934/934_151.htm

Raquel Garcia, Nuno Martins, Maria João Cabrita. Putative Markers of Adulteration in Olive Oil: Prospects and Limitations. *Food Research International* (2013) DOI: 10.1016/j.foodres.2013.05.008

In: Food Science Research ... Volume 1
Editor: Lucille Monaco Cacioppo

ISBN: 978-1-63117-932-7
© 2014 Nova Science Publishers, Inc.

Chapter 5

MARIA HELENE GIOVANETTI CANTERI

Affiliation: Federal University of Technology - Paraná (UTFPR)

Contact Point: Av. Monteiro Lobato, Km. 04

Date of Birth: 28/09/1971

Education: Doctor (PhD) Food Technology- UFPR and Sciences Agricultural (UAPV-France)

Research and Professional Experience: Food Biochemistry Teacher since 1996; Researcher about pectin from Brazilian fruits wastes since 2003

Professional Appointments:
Research experience at INRA (France)-Nov./2008 to Juin/ 2009

Publications Last 3 Years:
Canteri, Maria H. G. ; MORENO, LIRIAN ; WOSIACKI, Gilvan ; SCHEER, AGNES DE P. . Pectina: da matéria-prima ao produto final. Polímeros (São Carlos. Impresso), v. 22, p. 149-157, 2012.
SCHIEHL, A. R. ; PILATTI, L. A. ; CANTERI, M.H.G. ; VASCONCELOS, L. L. . QUALIDADE DE VIDA NO TRABALHO E SAÚDE: EVOLUÇÃO HISTÓRICA E PERSPECTIVAS DE INOVAÇÃO. Trabalho & Educação (UFMG), v. 21, p. 113-127, 2012.
CANTERI, Maria Helene ; Scheer, A.P. ; GINIES, C. ; Reich, M. ; RENARD, C.M.C.G. ; WOSIACKI, G. ; WOSIACKI, G. . RHEOLOGICAL AND MACROMOLECULAR QUALITY OF PECTIN EXTRACTED WITH NITRIC ACID FROM PASSION FRUIT RIND. Journal of Food Process Engineering, v. 35, p. 800-809, 2012.

Windson I Haminiuk, Charles ; Sierakowski, Maria-Rita ; S V Plata-Oviedo, Manuel ; Guilherme Branco, Ivanise ; Helene G Canteri, Maria ; Lucia Masson, Maria . ESTUDO DO COMPORTAMENTO REOLÓGICO DE SUCOS COMBINADOS DE FRUTAS VERMELHAS. Revista brasileira de tecnologia agroindustrial, v. 5, p. 314-325, 2011.

Sato, Mariana De Fátima ; Rigoni, Dayana Carla ; Canteri, Maria Helene Giovanetti ; Petkowicz, Carmen Lúcia de Oliveira ; Nogueira, Alessandro ; WOSIACKI, Gilvan . Chemical and instrumental characterization of pectin from dried pomace of eleven apple cultivars. Acta Scientiarum. Agronomy (Online), v. 33, p. 383-389, 2011.

Helene Giovanetti Canteri, Maria ; de Paula Scheer, Agnes ; Ginies, Christian ; Marie-Genevieve Claire Renard, Catherine ; WOSIACKI, Gilvan ; CANTERI, Maria Helene . IMPORTÂNCIA DO TRATAMENTO TÉRMICO NA CASCA DE MARACUJÁ PARA EXTRAÇÃO DE PECTINA. Revista brasileira de tecnologia agroindustrial, v. 4, p. 109-121, 2010.

CANTERI, Maria Helene ; Scheer, Agnes P. ; WOSIACKI, Gilvan ; Ginies, Christian ; Reich, Marise ; Renard, Catherine M. C. G. . A Comparative Study of Pectin Extracted from Passion Fruit Rind Flours. Journal of Polymers and the Environment, v. 18, p. 593-599, 2010.

CANTERI, Maria Helene ; SCHEER, A. P. ; PETKOWICZ, ; GINIES, C. ; RENARD, C. M. G. C. ; WOSIACKI, Gilvan . Physicochemical composition of the yellow passion fruit pericarp fractions and respective pectic substances. Journal of Food and Nutrition Research, v. 49, p. 113-122, 2010.

Giovanetti Canteri, Maria Helene ; Nogueira, Alessandro ; Oliveira Petkowicz, Carmen Lucia de ; WOSIACKI, Gilvan . Characterization of Apple Pectin A Chromatographic Approach. In: Leonardo de Azevedo Calderon. (Org.). Characterization of Apple Pectin-A Chromatographic Approach. 1ed.: InTech, 2012, v. , p. 325-342.

In: Food Science Research ... Volume 1
Editor: Lucille Monaco Cacioppo

ISBN: 978-1-63117-932-7
© 2014 Nova Science Publishers, Inc.

Chapter 6

ANDRES E. CARRILLO

Affiliation: Department of Exercise Science, Chatham University, Pittsburgh, PA, USA

Date of Birth: July 5, 1981

Education:
Doctor of Philosophy in Health and Kinesiology, Purdue University, West Lafayette, IN, USA.
Specialization: Exercise immunology. Minor: Gerontology. Supervising Committee: Dr. Gerald C. Hyner (gerontology), Dr. Michael G. Flynn (exercise immunology), Dr. Dorothy Teegarden (nutrition), and Dr. Darlene A. Sedlock (exercise physiology). 2006 – 2010.

Master of Science in Health and Human Performance, Dalhousie University, Halifax, NS, Canada. Specialization: Environmental physiology. Supervising Committee: Dr. Stephen S. Cheung (thermal physiology), Dr. Phil Campagna (exercise physiology), and Dr. Rene J. Murphy (exercise physiology). 2004 – 2006.

Bachelor of Kinesiology (Honors), Brock University, St. Catharines, ON, Canada. Major: Exercise physiology. Supervisor: Dr. Panagiota Klentrou (applied physiology). 2000 – 2004.

Research and Professional Experience:
Research Assistant. Department of Foods and Nutrition, Purdue University, West Lafayette, IN, USA. 2009 – 2010.
Research Assistant. Department of Physical Education and Kinesiology, Brock University, St. Catharines, ON, Canada. 2005.
Research Assistant. Department of Sport and Exercise Science, University of Thessaly, Trikala, Greece. 2004.

Professional Appointments:

Assistant Professor, Department of Exercise Science, Chatham University, Pittsburgh, PA, USA. 2012 – Current.

Post Doctoral Fellowship, Center for Research and Technology Thessaly, Trikala, Greece. Supervisor: Dr. Andreas D. Flouris. Research theme: Environmental physiology, ageing thermal biology, and longevity. 2010 – 2012.

Publications Last 3 Years:

1. Carrillo A.E., Cheung S.S., and Flouris A.D. (In press). Autonomic nervous system modulation during accidental syncope induced by heat and orthostatic stress. Aviation, Space, and Environmental Medicine.
2. Carrillo A.E., Flynn M.G., Pinkston C., Markofski M.M., Jiang Y., Donkin S., and Teegarden D. (In press). Impact of vitamin D supplementation during a resistance training intervention on body composition, muscle function, and glucose tolerance in overweight and obese adults. Clinical Nutrition.
3. Flouris A.D., Metsios G.S., Carrillo A.E., Jamurtas A.Z., Stivaktakis P.D., Tzatzarakis M.N., Tsatsakis A.M., and Koutedakis Y. (2012). Respiratory and Immune Response to Maximal Physical Exertion following Exposure to Secondhand Smoke in Healthy Adults. PLoS One; 7(2): e31880.
4. Carrillo A.E., Flynn M.G., Pinkston C., Markofski M.M., Jiang Y., Donkin S., and Teegarden D. (2012). Vitamin D supplementation during exercise training does not alter inflammatory biomarkers in overweight and obese subjects. Eur J Appl Physiol; Aug; 112(8):3045-52.
5. Carrillo A.E., Cheung S.S., and Flouris A.D. (2011). A novel model to predict cutaneous finger blood flow via finger and rectal temperatures. Microcirculation; Nov; 18(8): 670-676.
6. Flouris A.D. and Carrillo A.E. (2011). Evolutionary adaptation to hypoxic environments. Journal of Applied Physiology; Nov; 111(5): 1520-1521.
7. Carrillo A.E., Koutedakis Y. and Flouris A.D. (2011). Early life mammalian biology and later life physical performance: maximising physiological adaptation. British Journal of Sports Medicine; Sep; 45(12): 1000-1001.
8. Carrillo A.E. and Flouris A.D. (2011). Emerging trends in estimating energy expenditure. Journal of Applied Physiology; Aug; 111(2): 612.
9. Carrillo A.E., Christodoulou V.X., Koutedakis Y., and Flouris A.D. (2011). Autonomic nervous system modulation during an archery competition in novice and experienced adolescent archers. Journal of Sports Sciences; Jun; 29(9): 913-917.
10. Flouris A.D. and Carrillo A.E. (2011). Influence of early life factors on elite performance. Journal of Applied Physiology; Jan; 110(1): 284.

In: Food Science Research ... Volume 1
Editor: Lucille Monaco Cacioppo

ISBN: 978-1-63117-932-7
© 2014 Nova Science Publishers, Inc.

Chapter 7

GABRIEL DAVIDOV PARDO

Affiliation: Public University of Navarre, Food Technology Department

Contact Point: Campus Arrosadia s/n Pamplona 31006 Spain

Date of Birth: June 12th 1979

Education: PhD in Food Science

Research and Professional Experience:
May 2013 – Present   Contributor Food Science Department Public University of Navarra, Spain
Activities: Supervisor of undergraduate research projects; Support for PhD candidates; Analysis of polyphenols; Analysis of bioavailability of polyphenols; Writing postdoctoral proposals and scientific papers.

May 2011 – April 2013   Researcher Public University of Navarra, Spain
Activities: Teaching; Supervisor of undergraduate research projects; Analysis of polyphenols; Microencapsulation of polyphenols; Addition of microcapsules into bakery products; Sensory evaluation; Analysis of bioavailability of polyphenols; Writing papers.

November 2007 – April 2011   Doctoral Fellow Public University of Navarra, Spain
Analysis of polyphenols; Microencapsulation of polyphenols; Addition of microcapsules into bakery products; Sensory evaluation; Analysis of bioavailability of polyphenols; Writing papers.

Professional Appointments:
Researcher

Publications Last 3 Years:

G. Bobo, G. Davidov-Pardo, C. Arroqui, P. Vírseda, M.R. Marín-Arroyo, M. Navarro. Intralaboratory validation of microplate methods for total phenolic content and antioxidant activity on polyphenolic extracts, and comparison with conventional spectrophotometric method. Food Chemistry. (Under review).

Gabriel Davidov-Pardo, Iñigo Arozarena, María R. Marín-Arroyo. Grape seed extract: additive and functional ingredient. Agro Food Industry Hi-Tech. (Accepted).

Suazo, Yader; Davidov-Pardo, Gabriel; Arozarena, Iñigo. Effect of Fermentation and Roasting on the Phenolic Concentration and Antioxidant Activity of Cocoa from Nicaragua. Journal of Quality. (Under review).

Davidov-Pardo G., Arozarena I., Marín-Arroyo M. R. (2013) Optimization of a Wall Material Formulation to Microencapsulate a Grape Seed Extract Using a Mixture Design of Experiments. Food and Bioprocess Technology. 6(4), 941-951

Davidov-Pardo G., Moreno M., Arozarena I., Marín-Arroyo M. R., Bleibaum R., Bruhn C. (2012) Sensory and Consumer Perception of the Addition of Grape Seed Extracts in Cookies. Journal of Food Science. 77(12) S430-S438.

Davidov-Pardo G., Arozarena I., Marín-Arroyo M. R. (2011) Kinetics of Thermal Modifications in a Grape Seed Extract. Journal of Agricultural and Food Chemistry. 59(13) 7211-7217.

Davidov-Pardo, G., Arozarena, I., & Marín-Arroyo, M. (2011). Stability of polyphenolic extracts from grape seeds after thermal treatments. European Food Research and Technology, 232(2) 211-220.

OTHER PUBLICATIONS

Gabriel Davidov-Pardo, Sheila Romo-Sánchez, Iñigo Arozarena, María Arévalo-Villena, María R. Marín-Arroyo. Preliminary study to immobilize β-glucosidase by ionic gelation. New perspectives in wine and viticulture research. Red Gienol. Editors: Fernando Calderón Fernández, Felipe Palomero Rodríguez, José Antonio Suárez-Lepe ISBN: 978-84-96709-13-3. Madrid, Spain. 2013.

Davidov-Pardo G., Arozarena I., Marín-Arroyo M. R. Elaboration of an Optimal Wall Material Formulation to Encapsulate a Grape Seed Extract Using a Mixture Design of Experiments. Proceedings of the 5th European workshop on food engineering and technology. ISBN 978-84-694-1553-5 Valencia, Spain. 2011

Gabriel Davidov-Pardo, Iñigo Arozarena María R. Marín-Arroyo. Kinetics of resveratrol changes after thermal treatments. Wine Active Compounds 2011. Proceedings of the WAC2011 international conference Eds. Chaire Unesco « Culture et Traditions du Vin » - ISBN: 2-9054284-302011. Beaune, France. 2011.

Davidov-Pardo G., Arozarena I., Marín-Arroyo M. R. Kinetics of Thermal Modifications in a Grape Seed Extract. 2010 EFFoST Annual Meeting Food and Health Abstract CD. PS 2.23 Dublin, Ireland. 2010.

In: Food Science Research ... Volume 1
Editor: Lucille Monaco Cacioppo

ISBN: 978-1-63117-932-7
© 2014 Nova Science Publishers, Inc.

Chapter 8

RODRIGO DE CAMPOS MACEDO

Affiliation: Brazilian Institute of Geography and Statistics

Date of Birth: 02/11/1978

Education: Doctor in Remote Sensing

Research and Professional Experience: Research and Professional Experience: Land Use and Cover Change (LUCC), Vegetation Mapping, Land Use Mapping, Environmental Valuation

Professional Appointments: National cadastre of addresses for statistical purposes - coordination in Santa Catarina

Publications Last 3 Years:

Macedo, R. C.; Moreira, M. Z.; Domingues, E.; Gama, Â. M. R. C.; Sanson, F. E. G.; Teixeira, F. W.; DIAS, F. P.; Yamaguchi, F. Y.; Jacintho, L. R. C. Land Cover and Land Use in Brazil and the Environmental-Economic Accounts System. In: X International Symposium On Spatial Accuracy Assessment In Natural Resources And Environmental Sciences, 2012, Florianópolis/SC. Proceedings. 2012, v. 1, p. 73-78.
http://urlib.net/J8LNKAN8RW/3D53G4G

Macedo, R. C.; Santos, J. R.; Fonseca, L. M. G.; Almeida, C. M.; Soares, J. V. Delimitação de Copas em Florestas Clonais de Eucalyptus sp. Através de Classificação Baseada em Objeto. Revista Técnica do IEP, v. 5, julho/2012, p. 37-43, 2012.
http://urlib.net/J8LNKAN8RW/3D53G3H

Macedo, R. C.; Santos, J. R.; Soares, J. V. Validação de Modelo Digital de Terreno em Área Florestal com Relevo Ondulado, Gerado a Partir de Dados LiDAR. RBC. Revista Brasileira de Cartografia, v. 65, n. 4, p. 695-702, 2013.
http://urlib.net/8JMKD3MGP3W/3FCLL4C

http://plutao.sid.inpe.br/col/sid.inpe.br/plutao/2013/12.12.18.36.10/doc/Macedo_et_al_R
BC_2.pdf

Macedo, R. C.; Santos, J. R.; Soares, J. V. TREEX (Tree Extractor) - Uma Ferramenta para
Análise de Dossel Florestal e Contagem de Árvores a Partir de Dados LiDAR. RBC.
Revista Brasileira de Cartografia, v. 65, n. 4, p. 673-680, 2013.
http://urlib.net/8JMKD3MGP3W/3FCLL4J
http://plutao.sid.inpe.br/col/sid.inpe.br/plutao/2013/12.12.18.36.16/doc/Macedo_et_al_R
BC_1.pdf

Macedo, R. C.; Almeida, C. M.; Santos, J. R.; Rudorff, B. F. T. Modelagem Dinâmica
Espacial das Alterações de Cobertura e Uso da Terra Relacionadas à Expansão
Canavieira. Boletim de Ciências Geodésicas, v. 19, n. 2, p. 313-337, abr.-jun. 2013. ISSN
1982-2170. doi: <10.1590/S1982-21702013000200009>.
http://urlib.net/J8LNKAN8RW/3E7UNNS

Macedo, R. C. Modelagem Dinâmica Espacial e Valoração das Alterações de Cobertura e
Uso da Terra Relacionadas à Expansão Canavieira. Tese (Doutorado em Sensoriamento
Remoto) - Instituto Nacional de Pesquisas Espaciais (sid.inpe.br/mtc-
m19/2013/09.06.18.13-TDI), São José dos Campos/SP, 2013, 266 p.
http://urlib.net/8JMKD3MGP7W/3EPSPRS

ISBN: 978-1-63117-932-7
© 2014 Nova Science Publishers, Inc.

Chapter 9

CARMEN LUCIA DE OLIVERA PETKOWICZ

Affiliation: Federal University of Parana (UFPR)

Contact Point: Cel Francisco H. dos Santos, s/n CP 19046 CEP 81531-980

Date of Birth: 9/18/1963

Education: PhD Biochemistry - UFPR

Research and Professional Experience: Professor at UFPR since 2002; Researcher on plant polysaccharides

Publications Last 3 Years:

1. ROVARIS, ÂNGELA ANGELONI ; BALSAMO, GEISI MELLO ; DE OLIVEIRA COSTA, ANA CAROLINA ; MAISONNAVE ARISI, ANA CAROLINA ; MICKE, GUSTAVO A. ; PIOVEZAN, MARCEL ; Petkowicz, Carmen L.O. ; AMANTE, EDNA REGINA . Chemical characterization of liquid residues from aqueous enzymatic extraction of soybean oil. Lebensmittel-Wissenschaft + Technologie / Food Science + Technology, v. 51, p. 51-58, 2013.

2. BENTO, JOÃO FRANCISCO ; MAZZARO, IRINEU ; DE ALMEIDA SILVA, LIA MAGALHÃES ; DE AZEVEDO MOREIRA, RENATO ; FERREIRA, MARÍLIA LOCATELLI CORREA ; Reicher, Fany; de oliveira petkowicz, carmen lúcia . Diverse patterns of cell wall mannan/galactomannan occurrence in seeds of the Leguminosae. Carbohydrate Polymers, v. 92, p. 192-199, 2013.

3. Vriesmann, Lúcia C. ; Petkowicz, Carmen L.O. . Highly acetylated pectin from cacao pod husks (Theobroma cacao L.) forms gel. Food Hydrocolloids, v. 33, p. 58-65, 2013.

4. LIMA, ROGÉRIO BARBOSA ; DOS SANTOS, TIAGO BENEDITO ; VIEIRA, LUIZ GONZAGA ESTEVES ; FERRARESE, MARIA DE LOURDES LÚCIO ; FERRARESE-FILHO, OSVALDO ;DONATTI, LUCÉLIA ; BOEGER, MARIA

REGINA TORRES ; Petkowicz, Carmen Lúcia de Oliveira . Heat stress causes alterations in the cell-wall polymers and anatomy of coffee leaves (Coffea arabica L.). Carbohydrate Polymers, v. 93, p. 135-143, 2013.

5. VIANNA-FILHO, RICARDO PADILHA ; PETKOWICZ, CARMEN LÚCIA OLIVEIRA ; Silveira, Joana Léa Meira . Rheological characterization of O/W emulsions incorporated with neutral and charged polysaccharides. Carbohydrate Polymers, v. 93, p. 266-272, 2013.
Citações:1|1

6. Dalonso, Nicole; Petkowicz, Carmen Lúcia de Oliveira . Guarana powder polysaccharides: Characterisation and evaluation of the antioxidant activity of a pectic fraction. Food Chemistry, v. 134, p. 1804-1812, 2012.
Citações:6|9

7. Vriesmann, Lúcia Cristina; TEOFILO, R. F. ; Petkowicz, Carmen Lúcia de Oliveira . Extraction and characterization of pectin from cacao pod husks (Theobroma cacao L.) with citric acid. Lebensmittel-Wissenschaft + Technologie / Food Science + Technology, v. 49, p. 108-116, 2012.
Citações:4

8. ROVARIS, A. A.; DIAS, C. O. ; CUNHA, I. P. ; SCAFF, R. M. C. ; FRANCISCO, A. ; Petkowicz, Carmen L. de O. ; AMANTE, E. R. . Chemical composition of solid waste and effect of enzymatic oil extraction on the microstructure of soybean (Glycine max). Industrial Crops and Products (Print), v. 36, p. 405-414, 2012.
Citações:2|2

9. Rosário, M. M.T.; AMARAL, A. E. ; NOLETO, G. R. ; PETKOWICZ, C. L. O. . Storage xiloglucans: potent macrophages activators. Chemico-Biological Interactions (Print), v. 189, p. 127-133, 2011.
Citações:2|4

10 .Vriesmann, Lúcia Cristina ; Teófilo, Reinaldo Francisco ; Petkowicz, Carmen Lúcia de Oliveira . Optimization of nitric acid-mediated extraction of pectin from cacao pod husks (Theobroma cacao L.) using response surface methodology. Carbohydrate Polymers, v. 84, p. 1230-1236, 2011.
Citações:14|16

11. Santos, T.B. ; BUDZINSKI, I. G. F. ; MARUR, C. J. ; Petkowicz, C.L.O. ; Pereira, L.F.P. ; VIEIRA, L. G. E. . Expression of three galactinol synthase isoforms in Coffea arabica L.and accumulation of raffinose and stachyose in response to abiotic stresses. Plant Physiology and Biochemistry (Paris), v. 49, p. 441-448, 2011.
Citações:15

In: Food Science Research … Volume 1
Editor: Lucille Monaco Cacioppo

ISBN: 978-1-63117-932-7
© 2014 Nova Science Publishers, Inc.

Chapter 10

LUCIANA DE SOUZA NEVES ELLENDERSEN

Affiliation: Federal University of Paraná/PNPD/CAPES

Contact Point: Rua: Joana Souza Gusso, 126 – 2 – CEP: 82560-050 – Curitiba – PR - Brazil

Date of Birth: 03/23/1976

Education: Post-Doctor (PhD) Food Engineering - UFPR

Research and Professional Experience: University professor of Food Science and Technology area and Sensory Analysis since 2002; Researcher in product development, sensory analysis, and in Food Science and Technology with fruits and yacon tuberous root.

Professional Appointments: PNPD researcher of CAPES/UFPR

Publications Last 3 Years:

KOTOVICZ, V. ; Ellendersen, L. S. N. ; CLARINDO, M. ; MASSON, M. L. . Influence of Process Conditions on the Kinetics of the Osmotic Dehydration of Yacon ( ) in Fructose Solution. Journal of Food Processing and Preservation, p. n/a-n/a, 2013.

de Souza Neves Ellendersen, Luciana ; GRANATO, DANIEL ; BIGETTI GUERGOLETTO, KARLA ; WOSIACKI, GILVAN . Development and sensory profile of a probiotic beverage from apple fermented with Lactobacillus casei. Engineering in Life Sciences (Print), v. 12, p. n/a-n/a, 2012. Citações:2|4

GRANATO, D. ; CASTRO, I. A. ; NEVES, L. S. ; MASSON, M. L. . Physical Stability Assessment And Sensory Optimization Of A Dairy-Free Emulsion Using Response Surface Methodology. Journal of Food Science, v. 75, p. S149-S155, 2010.

NEVES, L. S. ; Wosiacki, G. . Análise Sensorial Descritiva Quantitativa - estatística e interpretação. 1. ed. Ponta Grossa: UEPG, 2010. 90p .

In: Food Science Research ... Volume 1
Editor: Lucille Monaco Cacioppo

ISBN: 978-1-63117-932-7
© 2014 Nova Science Publishers, Inc.

Chapter 11

LINDA A. DEGRAFFENRIED

Affiliation: Department of Nutritional Sciences, The University of Texas at Austin

Contact Point: 1400 Barbara Jordan Blvd., DPRI R1800, Austin, TX 78723

Education: PhD in Molecular Medicine, UT Health Science Center at San Antonio

Research and Professional Experience:

2001-2002	Postdoctoral Fellow, Division of Medical Oncology, University of Texas Health Science Center at San Antonio, San Antonio, Texas
2002-2003	Instructor, Division of Medical Oncology, University of Texas Health Science Center at San Antonio, San Antonio, Texas
2002-present	Member, Cancer Treatment and Research Center at UTHSCSA
2002-present	Member, Southwest Oncology Group
2003 – 2008	Assistant Professor, Division of Medical Oncology, University of Texas Health Science Center at San Antonio, San Antonio, Texas
2008 – present	Associate Professor, Department of Nutritional Sciences, University of Texas, Austin, TX
2008 – present	Adjunct Associate Professor, Department of Cellular and Structural Biology, UTHSCSA, San Antonio, TX
2009 – present	Adjunct Associate Professor, Department of Carcinogenesis, UT-MD Anderson Cancer Center, Smithville, TX

Publications Last 3 Years:

1. Cavazos DA, Salcedo Price M, Apte S, deGraffenried, LA. Docohexanoic Acid Selectively Induces Human Prostate Cancer Cell Sensitivity to Oxidative Stress through Modulation of NF-êB. Prostate, 71(13):1420-8 2011.

2. Mishra S, Tang Y, Wang L, deGraffenried L, Yeh I-Y, Werner S, Troyer D, Copland JA, Sun L-Z. Blockade of transforming growth factor-beta (TGFâ) signaling inhibits osteoblastic tumorigenesis by a novel human prostate cancer cell line. Prostate, Feb 14 2011. doi: 10.1002/pros.21361

3. Tiwary R, Yu W, Degraffenried LA, Sanders BG, Kline K. Targeting cholesterol-rich microdomains to circumvent tamoxifen-resistant breast cancer. Breast Cancer Res. 13(6):R120, 2011

4. Friedrichs W, Ruparel SB, Marciniak RA, and deGraffenried L. Omega-3 Fatty Acid Inhibition of Prostate Cancer Progression to Hormone Independence is Associated with Suppression of mTOR Signaling and Androgen Receptor Expression. Nutr and Cancer, 63 (5), 2011

5. De Angel RE, Conti CJ, Wheatley KE, Brenner AJ, Otto G, Degraffenried LA, Hursting SD. The enhancing effects of obesity on mammary tumor growth and Akt/mTOR pathway activation persist after weight loss and are reversed by RAD001. Mol Carcinog. 2012 Jan 30. doi: 10.1002/mc.21878.

6. Chen CH, deGraffenried LA. Anethole suppressed cell survival and induced apoptosis in human breast cancer cells independent of estrogen receptor status. Phytomedicine. 19(8-9):763-7, 2012

7. Price R S, Cavazos D A, De Angel R E, Hursting S D and deGraffenried LA. Obesity-related systemic factors promote an invasive phenotype in prostate cancer cells. Prostate Cancer Prostatic Dis 2012 Jun;15(2):135-43. doi: 10.1038/pcan.2011.54

8. Apte S, Cavazos D, Whelan K and deGraffenried L. A low dietary ratio of omega-6 to omega-3 fatty acids may delay progression of prostate cancer. Nutr and Cancer, *in press*

9. De Angulo A, Faris R, Cavazos D, Jolly C, Daniel B and deGraffenried L. Age-related Alterations in T-lymphocytes Modulate Key Pathways in Prostate Tumorigenesis. Prostate, *in press*

In: Food Science Research ... Volume 1
Editor: Lucille Monaco Cacioppo

ISBN: 978-1-63117-932-7
© 2014 Nova Science Publishers, Inc.

Chapter 12

PRISCILA FARAGE DE GOUVEIA

Affiliation: University of Brasilia

Date of Birth: 04/15/1989

Education:

Gr., Nutrition, University of Brasilia, 2011
Currently attending master's degree on Human Nutrition, University of Brasilia

Research and Professional Experience:

Nutritional counseling for patients with celiac disease at the Brasilia's University Hospital
Member of the Brazil's Celiac Association – Distrito Federal

Professional Appointments:

Participation in the project: "Center for Research, Diagnosis, Treatment and Support for Patients with Celiac Disease"

Publications Last 3 Years:

Laporte L, Zandonadi RP. Chefs' knowledgement about coeliac disease. Alimentos e Nutrição. 2012;22:465-470.
Zandonadi RP, Botelho RA, Gandolfi L, Ginani JS, Montenegro F, Pratesi R. Green banana pasta: an alternative for gluten-free diets. Journal of the American Dietetic Association. 2012;112:1068-1072.
Vieira AR, Dias AR, Cunha AGF, Hargreaves SM, Santos SGS, Botelho RBA, Zandonadi RP. Massa de empada sem glúten e sem leite, enriquecida com biomassa de banana verde. Nutrição Brasil. 2011;10:175-178.

Araújo HMC, Araújo WMC, Botelho RBA, Zandonadi RP. Celiac disease, eating habits and practices and life quality of life. Revista de Nutrição. 2010;23:467-474.

Ginani VC, Ginani JS, Botelho RBA, Zandonadi RP, Akutsu RC, Araujo WMC. Reducing fat content of brazilian traditional preparations does not alter food acceptance: development of a model for fat reduction that conciliates health and culture. Journal of Culinary Science & Technology. 2010;8:229-241.

Zandonadi RP. Glúten e individualidade bioquímica. Brazilian Journal of Functional Nutrition. 2010;11:54-60.

Zandonadi RP, Botelho RA. Macarrão sem glúten (com psyllium). Brazilian Journal of Functional Nutrition. 2010;11:62-62.

Cunha JG, Oliveira PSG, Mendes TG, Ginani JS, Zandonadi RP. Efeitos dos diferentes tipos de processadores domésticos na produção de suco de frutas e seu impacto na curva glicêmica. Alimentos e Nutrição. 2010;21:63-68.

Felinto VT, Almeida RC, Paiva AL, Garcez N, Zandonadi RP. Análise da rotulagem de chocolates quanto à presença de glúten. Higiene Alimentar. 2010;24:182-186.

Teixeira AP, Melo GR, Zandonadi RP. Aceitação e percepção dos estudantes de gastronomia e nutrição em relação aos alimentos funcionais. Alimentos e Nutrição. 2010;21:367-372.

Zandonadi RP, Botelho RA, Araújo WMC. Psyllium as a substitute for gluten in bread. Journal of the American Dietetic Association. 2009;109:1781-1784.

Zandonadi RP, Resende AJ, Teixeira AP, Paiva CF. O efeito da adição de batata yacon no suco de laranja industrializado na curva glicêmica de estudantes universitários. Alimentos e Nutrição. 2009;20:313-319.

In: Food Science Research ... Volume 1
Editor: Lucille Monaco Cacioppo

ISBN: 978-1-63117-932-7
© 2014 Nova Science Publishers, Inc.

Chapter 13

RAQUEL MARTA NEVES DOS SANTOS GARCIA

Affiliation: ICAAM, Évora University

Contact Point: Laboratorio de Enologia, Nucleo da Mitra, Universidade de Évora, Ap 94 7002-554 Évora

Date of Birth: 19th May, 1974

Education: Ph.D.

Research and Professional Experience: Assistant Researcher at Évora University-ICAAM

Professional Appointments: Mainly dedicated to research on olive oil and wines at Évora University

Publications Last 3 Years:

Marco Gomes Da Silva, Ana Maria Costa Freitas, Maria João Bastos Cabrita and Raquel Garcia. (2012) "Olive oil composition: volatiles compound" pp. 17- 46 In Olive Oil - Constituents, Quality, Health Properties and Bioconversions, p 510, ISBN 978-953-307-921-9 Edited by Prof. Boskou Dimitrios; Publisher Intech, Publication date: February 2012, Subject: Life Sciences - DOI: 10.5772/28512
http://www.intechopen.com/articles/show/title/oil-composition-volatiles

Maria João Bastos Cabrita, Raquel Garcia, Nuno Martins, Marco Gomes Da Silva and Ana Maria Costa Freitas (2012) "Gas chromatography in analysis of compounds released from wood into wine" pp 185-298 In Advanced Gas Chromatography - Progress in Agricultural, Biomedical and Industrial Applications, p 460 ISBN 978-953-51-0298-4 Edited by Prof. Mustafa Ali Mohd; Publisher Intech, Publication date: March 2012, Subject: Analytical Chemistry - DOI: 10.5772/32659
http://www.intechopen.com/articles/show/title/gas-chromatography-in-analysis-of-compounds-released-from-wood-into-wine

Raquel Garcia, Maria João Cabrita, Ana Maria Costa Freitas. Application of Molecularly Imprinted Polymers for the analysis of pesticide residues in food- a highly selective and innovative approach *American Journal of Analytical Chemistry* 2, 16-25 (2011) http://dx.doi.org/10.4236/ajac.2011.228119

Raquel Garcia, Bruno Soares, Cristina Barrocas Dias, Ana Maria Costa Freitas, Maria João Cabrita. Phenolic and Furanic Compounds of Portuguese Chestnut and French, American and Portuguese Oak Wood Chips. *European Food Research and Technology* 235, 457-467 (2012) DOI: 10.1007/s00217-012-1771-2

Bruno Soares; Raquel Garcia; Ana Maria Costa Freitas; Maria João Cabrita. Phenolic compounds released from oak, cherry, chestnut and robinia chips into a syntethic wine: influence of toasting level. *Ciência e Técnica Vitivinicola / Journal of Viticulture and Enology.* 27 (1): 17-26 (2012)

Nuno Martins; Raquel Garcia; Marco Gomes Da Silva; Maria João Cabrita. Volatiles compounds from oak, cherry, chestnut and acacia chips: influence of toasting level. *Ciência e Técnica Vitivinicola / Journal of Viticulture and Enology.* 27 (1): 49-57 (2012)

Rodrigo Silva, Filipe Folgosa, Paulo Soares, Alice S. Pereira, Raquel Garcia, Juan Jesus Gestal-Otero, Pedro Tavares, Marco D.R. Gomes da Silva. "Occupational cosmic radiation exposure in Portuguese airline pilots: study of a possible correlation with oxidative biological markers", Radiat. Environ. Biophys. (2013), DOI: 10.1007/s00411-013-0460-2.

Raquel Garcia, Nuno Martins, Maria João Cabrita. Putative Markers of Adulteration in Olive Oil: Prospects and Limitations. *Food Research International* (2013) DOI: 10.1016/j.foodres.2013.05.008

In: Food Science Research ... Volume 1
Editor: Lucille Monaco Cacioppo

ISBN: 978-1-63117-932-7
© 2014 Nova Science Publishers, Inc.

Chapter 14

FEDERICA GRAZIANO

Affiliation: Department of Human and Social Science, University of Aosta Valley, Italy

Contact Point: Strada Cappuccini, 2A - 11100 Aosta - ITALY

Date of Birth: March 10, 1976

Education: Degree in Psychology, Ph.D. in Social and Developmental Psychology

Research and Professional Experience:
Risk behavior in adolescence

The protective role of family and school experience in adolescence

Peer and romantic relationships in adolescence

Effectiveness of risk prevention and health promotion programs targeting adolescents

Professional Appointments:
Post doc at the University of Turin

Contract professor at the University of Turin and at the University of Aosta Valley

Consultant Psychologist

Publications Last 3 Years:

1. Graziano, F., Bina, M., Giannotta, F., Ciairano, S. (2012). Drinking motives and alcoholic beverage preferences among Italian adolescent. *Journal of Adolescence, 35,* 823-831.
2. Cattelino, E., Calandri, E., Bina, M., Graziano, F. (2011). Fattori di protezione nei confronti di pari devianti in adolescenza [Protective factors from deviant peers in adolescence]. Nucleo Monotematico: Aspetti adattivi e disadattavi nelle relazioni tra pari dalla fanciullezza all' adolescenza, *Giornale di Psicologia dello Sviluppo, 98,* 104-115.
3. Bina, M, Borca, G., Begotti, T. Graziano, F. Bonino, S. (2011). Promuovere la salute sessuale in adolescenza. Evidenze di efficacia e linee metodologiche di intervento [Sexual health promotion in adolescence: evidence of effectiveness and methodological guidelines for intervention]. *Giornale di Psicologia dello Sviluppo, 100,* 21-36.
4. Graziano, F., Bina, M., Ciairano, S. (2010). Le funzioni del consumo di tabacco e alcolici percepite dagli adolescenti: una ricerca con il focus group [The functions of cigarettes smoking and alcohol use in the adolescents' perception: a research based on focus groups]. *Psicologia della Salute, 3,* 9-30.
5. Graziano, F., Geninatti, S., Pertosa, M.A, Consoli, A (2010). Il rifiuto sociale in preadolescenza: il ruolo del rendimento scolastico, del comportamento prosociale e dell' autoefficacia percepita [Social rejection in preadolescence: the role of school achievement, prosocial behavior and perceived self-efficacy]. *Eta Evolutiva, 95,* 5-13.

In: Food Science Research ... Volume 1
Editor: Lucille Monaco Cacioppo

ISBN: 978-1-63117-932-7
© 2014 Nova Science Publishers, Inc.

Chapter 16

TATSUYA HAYASHI

Affiliation: Laboratory of Sports and Exercise Medicine, Graduate School of Human and Environmental Studies, Kyoto University

Date of Birth: 10/7/1960

Education:

1986 M.D.   Kyoto University, Faculty of Medicine

1996 Ph.D.   Doctor of Medical Science
                 Department of Medicine and Clinical Science, Kyoto University, Graduate School of Medicine, Address: Graduate School of Human and Environmental Studies, Kyoto University, Yoshida-nihonmatsu-cho, Sakyo-ku, Kyoto, 606-8501, Japan

Research and Professional Experience:

1996-1999   Research Fellow, Section on Metabolism, Joslin Diabetes Center, Boston, Massachusetts, U.S.A.

Professional Appointments:

1999-2004   Assistant Professor, Department of Medicine and Clinical Science, Kyoto University Graduate School of Medicine
2004-2012   Associate Professor, Graduate School of Human & Environmental Studies, Kyoto University
2012-   Professor, Graduate School of Human & Environmental Studies, Kyoto University

Publications Last 3 Years:

Miyamoto L, Egawa T, Oshima R, Kurogi E, Tomida Y, Tsuchiya K, Hayashi T. AICAR stimulation metabolome-widely mimics electrical contraction in isolated rat epitrochlearis muscle. Am J Physiol Cell Physiol. (in press)

Ma X, Tsuda S, Yang X, Gu N, Tanabe H, Oshima R, Matsushita T, Egawa T, Dong A, Zhu B, Hayashi T. Pu-erh tea hot water extract activates Akt and induces insulin-independent glucose transport in rat skeletal muscle. J Med Food. 16:1-4, 2013.

Miyamoto L, Ebihara K, Kusakabe T, Aotani D, Yamamoto-Kataoka S, Sakai T, Aizawa-Abe M, Yamamoto Y, Fujikura J, Hayashi T, Hosoda K, Nakao K. Leptin activates hepatic 5'AMP-Activated Protein Kinase through sympathetic nervous system and $f_\zeta 1$ adrenergic receptor: A potential mechanism for improvement of fatty liver in lipodystrophy by leptin. J Biol Chem. 287:40441-7, 2012.

Egawa T, Masuda S, Goto K, Hayashi T. Increased dystrophin mRNA and protein levels in atrophic skeletal muscles in streptozotocin-induced diabetic rat. J Phys Fit Sport Med. 1: 709-13, 2012.

Tsuda S, Egawa T, Ma X, Oshima R, Kurogi E, Hayashi T. Coffee polyphenol caffeic acid but not chlorogenic acid increases 5'AMP-activated protein kinase and insulin-independent glucose transport in rat skeletal muscle. J Nutr Biochem. 23: 1403-9, 2012.

Takaishi T, Imaeda K, Tanaka T, Moritani T, Hayashi T. A short bout of stair climbing/descending exercise attenuates postprandial hyperglycemia in middle-aged males with impaired glucose tolerance. Appl Physiol Nutr Metab. 37:193-6, 2012.

Toyoda T, Egawa T, Hayashi T. Metabolic sensor for low intensity exercise: insights from AMPK$f_\zeta 1$ activation in skeletal muscle. J Phys Fitness Sports Med. 1:59-64, 2012.

Egawa T, Ma X, Hamada T, Hayashi T. Chapter 90: Caffeine and Insulin-Independent Glucose Transport. In: Tea in Health and Disease Prevention (Preedy VR ed.), Academic Press, 1077-88, 2012.

Egawa T, Tsuda S, Ma X, Hamada T, Hayashi T. Caffeine modulates phosphorylation of insulin receptor substrate (IRS)-1 and impairs insulin signal transduction in rat skeletal muscle. J Appl Physiol. 111: 1629-36, 2011.

Ma X, Egawa T, Oshima R, Kurogi E, Tanabe H, Tsuda S, Hayashi T. Coptidis rhizoma water extract stimulates 5'-AMP-activated protein kinase in rat skeletal muscle. Chin J Nat Med. 9: 215-21, 2011.

Egawa T, Hamada H, Ma X, Karaike K, Kameda N, Masuda S, Iwanaka N, Hayashi T. Caffeine activates preferentially α 1-isoform of 5'AMP-activated protein kinase in rat skeletal muscle. Acta Physiol (Oxf). 201: 227-38, 2011.

In: Food Science Research ... Volume 1
Editor: Lucille Monaco Cacioppo

ISBN: 978-1-63117-932-7
© 2014 Nova Science Publishers, Inc.

Chapter 17

MARÍA JESÚS LAGARDA BLANCH

Affiliation: Food Science and Nutrition Area. Faculty of Pharmacy. University of Valencia (Spain)

Contact Point: Faculty of Pharmacy. Avd/ Vicente Andrés Estellés s/n Burjassot 46100. Spain; M.J.Lagarda@uv.es

Date of Birth: January 21, 1957

Education: Ph Pharmacy (Food Science)

Research and Professional Experience: Contents, stability, bioavailability and bioactivity in bioactive compounds (trace elements, plant sterols, gangliosides, antioxidants, etc.)

Professional Appointments: Full Professor

Publications Last 3 Years:

Cilla, A., Perales, S, Lagarda M.J., Barbera, R., Clemente, G., Farré, R., Influence of storage and in vitro gastrointestinal digestion on total antioxidant capacity of fruit beverages. J.Food Composition and Analysis, 24, 8794 (2011)

Gonzalez-Larena, M., García-Llatas, G., Vidal, C., Sanchez-Siles, L.M., Barbera,R., Lagarda, M.J., Stability of Plant Sterols in Ingredients Used in Functional Foods, J. Agric. Food Chem., 59, 3624-31 (2011)

Hernández-Mijares, A., Bañuls, C., Jover, A., Solá, E., Bellod, L., Martínez-Triguero, M.L., Lagarda, M.J., Víctor, V.M., Rocha, M., Low intestinal cholesterol absorption is associated with a reduced efficacy of phytosterol esters as hypolipemic agents in patients with metabolic syndrome. Clin. Nutr. 30, 604-609 (2011)

Lacomba R. Salcedo J. Alegria A. Barbera R. Hueso P. Matencio E. Lagarda MJ., Effect of simulated gastrointestinal digestion on sialic acid and gangliosides present in human milk and infant formulas, , J. Agric Food Chem., 59, 5755-62 (2011)

Salcedo, J., Lacomba, R., Alegría, A., Barbera, R., Matencio, E., Lagarda, M.J., Comparison of spectrophotometric and HPLC methods for determining sialic acid in infant formulas, Food Chem., 127, 1905 " 10 (2011)

Lacomba, R., Salcedo, J., Alegría, A., Barberá, R., Hueso, P., Matencio, E., Lagarda, M.J., Sialic acid (N-acetyl and N-glycolylneuraminic acid) and ganglioside in whey protein concentrates and infant formulae. Int. Dairy J., 21, 887 895 (2011)

Cilla, A., Lagarda, MJ., Alegría, A., De Ancos, B., Cano, MP., Sánchez-Moreno, C., Plaza, L., Barberá, R. Effect of processing and food matrix on calcium and phosphorous bioavailability from milk-based fruit beverages in Caco-2 cells. Food Research International 44, 3030-3038 (2011)

García-Llatas, G., Vidal, A., Cilla, A., Barberá, R., Lagarda, M.J., Simultaneous quantification of serum phytosterols and cholesterol precursors using a simple gas chromatographic method, Eur J Lipid Sci Technol, 114, 520526 (2012).

Alemany-Costa, L., González-Larena, M., García-Llatas, G., Alegría A., Barberá, R., Sánchez-Siles, LM, Lagarda., MJ, Sterol stability in functional fruit beverages enriched with different plant sterol sources, Food Res Int 48 265270 (2012)

González-Larena, M., Cilla, A., García-Llatas, G., Barberá, R., Lagarda, M.J., Plant sterols and antioxidant parameters in enriched beverages: storage stability. J. Agric. Food Chem. 60, 4725-4734 (2012)

García-Llatas G, Alegría A, Barberá R, Lagarda MJ, Farré R. "Minerals" (Chapter 31), en "Handbook of Analysis of Active Compounds in Functional Foods". CRC Press; Leo M.L. Nollet y Fidel Toldrá editores. ISBN: 978-1-4398-1588-5. 2012. Pags: 689-722.

Cilla, A., Alegría. A., de Ancos, B., Sanchez- Moreno, C., Cano, MP., Plaza, L., Clemente, G., Lagarda, M.J., Barberá, R. Bioaccessibility of tocopherols, carotenoids, and ascorbic acid from milk- and soy-based fruit beverages: influence of food matrix and processing. J. Agric. Food Chem., 60, 7282-7290 (2012)

Lacomba, R., Cilla, A., Alegria, A., Barberá, R., Silvestre, D., Lagarda, M.J., Stability of fatty acids tocopherols during cold storage of human milk. Int. Dairy J. 27, 22 26 (2012).

Salcedo, J., Barberá, R., Materncio, E., Alegría, A., Lagarda, M.J., Gangliosides and sialic acid effects upon newborn pathogenic bacteria adhesion: An in vitro study. Food Chem. 136, 726 7334 (2013).

García-Llatas, G., Cilla, A., Higueras, L., Pons, M., Ripollés, S., Bañuls, C., Lagarda, M.J., The effect of enriching milk-based beverages with plant sterols on the fatty acid composition of the products. Int. J. Dairy Technol. 66, (2013) doi: 10.1111/0307.12068

In: Food Science Research ... Volume 1
Editor: Lucille Monaco Cacioppo

ISBN: 978-1-63117-932-7
© 2014 Nova Science Publishers, Inc.

Chapter 18

ZHEN MA

Affiliation: College of Food Engineering and Nutritional Science, Shaanxi Normal University, Shaanxi, China, 710062

Contact Point: 3630 119 St NW Apt 307, Edmonton, Alberta, T6J 2X6, Canada

Date of Birth: August, 18, 1986

Education: Ph.D. degree (graduated from McGill University)

Research and Professional Experience: Student Affiliated Research assistant and postdoctoral fellow at Food Research and Development Centre, Agriculture and Agri-Food Canada since May, 2009 to April, 2013.

Professional Appointments: Postdoctoral fellow

Publications Last 3 Years:

Ma, Z., Boye, J. I., Simpson, B. K., Prasher, S. O., Montpetit, D., & Malcolmson, L. (2011). Thermal processing effects on the functional properties and microstructure of lentil, chickpea, and pea flours. *Food Research International*, 44(8): 2534-2544.

Ma, Z., Boye, J. I. (2013) Advances in the design and production of reduced-fat and reduced-cholesterol salad dressing and mayonnaise: A review. *Food and Bioprocess Technology*, 6(3): 648-670.

Ma, Z., Boye, J. I., Fortin J., Simpson, B. K., Prasher, S. O. (2013) Rheological, physical stability, microstructural and sensory properties of salad dressings supplemented with raw and thermally treated lentil flours. *Journal of Food Engineering*, 116(4): 862-872.

Ma, Z., Boye, J. I., (2013). Microstructure, physical stability, and rheological properties of model salad dressing emulsions supplemented with various types of pulse flours. *Journal of Food Research*, 2(2): 167-181.

Boye, J. I., Ma, Z. (2012). Finger on the pulse. *Food Science & Technology (London)*, (ISSN: 1475-3324), *26*(2): 20-24.

Dong, J., Ma, X., Ma, Z., Fu, Z., Wei, Q., Qiu, G., (2012). Effects of green-keeping treatment on the functional constituents in flower tea of *Eucommia ulmoides*. *Industrial Crops and Products*, 36(1): 389-394.

Ma, Z., Boye, J. I. Novel health ingredients and their applications in food emulsions and salad dressings (Chapter 5). In: Nutraceutical and Functional Food Processing Technology. (J. I. Boye et al. ed.). Wiley-Blackwell (Expected to be published in December, 2013).

Boye, J. I., Ma, Z. Advances in legume processing perspective from North American Food Industry. In: Food Processing: Principles and Applications, 2nd edition. (S. Clark, S. Jung, & B. Lamsal, eds.). Wiley-Blackwell (Expected to be published in September, 2013).

Boye, J. I., Ma, Z. (2013). Impact of processing on health related compounds of field peas. In: Processing and Impact on Active Components in Food (V. R. Preedy ed.). Springer Publishing Company (Expected to be published in December, 2013).

Simpson, B. K., Ackaah-Gyasi N. A., Patel P., Ducharme J., Ma, Z., Yin F. H. (2013). Enzymes and Inhibitors in Food and Health. In: Recent Developments in Biotechnology (J. N. Govil et al. ed.). Studium Press LLC (Expected to be published in January, 2014).

In: Food Science Research ... Volume 1
Editor: Lucille Monaco Cacioppo

ISBN: 978-1-63117-932-7
© 2014 Nova Science Publishers, Inc.

Chapter 19

FLÁVIA ROBERTA BUSS MARENDA

Affiliation: State University of Ponta Grossa (UEPG)

Contact Point: Av. Carlos Cavalcanti, 4748 – CEP 84030-900 – Ponta Grossa – PR - Brazil

Date of Birth: 05/02/1992

Education: Master in Food Technology – UEPG

Research and Professional Experience: Researcher about pectin from Brazilian fruits wastes in 2013.

Professional Appointments: Student

Publications Last 3 Years:

MARENDA, F. R. B. ; ROGGENBACK, J. ; FERREIRA, V. S. ; CANTERI, M. H. G. Meatball development and evaluation of beef with added okara. Oral Presentation Work –CONAITEC, 2012.

CHAVES, C. P. ; MARENDA, F. R. B. ; BITTENCOURT, J. V. M. ; CANTERI, M. H. G.Gluten-free products available for celiac consumers. 2013. (Poster Presentation Work - I MOSTRA ALIMENTOS UTFPR).

CHAVES, C. P. ; MARENDA, F. R. B. ; SANTOS, T. P. M. ; BITTENCOURT, J. V. M. ; CANTERI, M. H. G. Food sources alternative for celiac consumers. 2013. (Poster Presentation Work – I MOSTRA ALIMENTOS UTFPR).

MARENDA, F. R. B. ; SILVA, L. ; MORAES, R. A. ; FERREIRA, B. L. ; CANTERI, M. H. G. Partial characterization and determination of phenolics compounds of peel flour yellow passion fruit. Oral Presentation Work - I MOSTRA ALIMENTOS UTFPR, 2013.

MARENDA, F. R. B. ; CANTERI, M. H. G. Efficiency extraction and determination of phenolics of pectic from peel flour yellow passion fruit. Oral Presentation Work - I MOSTRA ALIMENTOS UTFPR, 2013.

RODRIGUES, S. A. ; MARENDA, F. R. B. ; CANTERI, M. H. G. 10 steps for implementation of HACCP (Hazard Analysis and Critical Control Points)in food production chain. Poster Presentation Work - I MOSTRA ALIMENTOS UTFPR, 2013.

In: Food Science Research ... Volume 1
Editor: Lucille Monaco Cacioppo

ISBN: 978-1-63117-932-7
© 2014 Nova Science Publishers, Inc.

Chapter 20

FERNANDA MATTIODA

Affiliation: Federal University of Technology - Paraná (UTFPR)

Contact Point: Av. Monteiro Lobato, Km. 04 – Ponta Grossa – PR - Brazil

Date of Birth: 04/18/1985

Education: Master in Production Engineering- UTFPR

Research and Professional Experience: Food Technology Teacher since 2013

Professional Appointments: Researcher since 2011 (UTFPR).

Publications Last 3 Years:

MATTIODA, F. ; BITTENCOURT, J. V. M. ; FRANCISCO, A. C. ; PINHEIRO, K. H. ; BAPTISTA, F. S. . Treinamento higiênico-sanitário na produção leiteira: Estudo de caso em agricultores familiares no Sudeste do Paraná. Revista do Instituto de Laticínios Cândido Tostes, v. 67, p. 30-40, 2012.

HOOGERHEIDE, Suzanna L. ; MATTIODA, F. . Qualidade Microbiológica do leite cru refrigerado em propriedades leiteiras do estado do Paraná. Revista do Instituto de Laticínios Cândido Tostes, v. 67, p. 58-63, 2012.

MATTIODA, F. ; BITTENCOURT, J. V. M. ; Kovaleski, J. L. . Qualidade do leite de pequenas propriedades rurais de Fernandes Pinheiro e Teixeira Soares - PR. Revista ADMpg (Online), v. 4, p. 1-9, 2011.

MATTIODA, F. ; DOMINGUES, Flávia ; TEDRUS, Guilherme de A. S. ; CANEDO, Juan Cássio ; RODRIGUES, J. A. S. ; PEREIRA, Lara T. P. ; TRANCOSO JUNIOR, R. F. ; BARROS, Solange A. B. de M. . Avaliação inicial da água nas propriedades leiteiras de Teixeira Soares - PR. CCNExt - Revista de Extensão, v. 1, p. 37-44, 2010.

SAMULAK, R. L. ; BITTENCOURT, J. V. M. ; Kovaleski, J. L. ; MATTIODA, F. . Obstáculos na implantação de boas práticas de fabricação em frigorífico de abate de suínos e fabricação de embutidos. In: 6 Encontro de Engenharia e Tecnologia dos Campos Gerais, 2011, Ponta Grossa. 6 Encontro de Engenharia e Tecnologia dos Campos Gerais, 2011.

PINHEIRO, K. H. ; BITTENCOURT, J. V. M. ; MATTIODA, F. . A model for traceability of organic products from Brazilian smallholders farming. In: III Ciclo de Atualização Agropecuária da 34ª Exposição Feira Agropecuária e Industrial de Ponta Grossa, 2011, Ponta Grossa. III Ciclo de Atualização Agropecuária, 2011.

MATTIODA, F. ; BITTENCOURT, J. V. M. ; PINHEIRO, K. H. . Transferência de informação e tecnologia a agricultores familiares: Estudo multicaso no Sudeste do Paraná. In: III Ciclo de Atualização Agropecuária da 34ª Exposição Feira Agropecuária e Industrial de Ponta Grossa, 2011, Ponta Grossa. III Ciclo de Atualização Agropecuária, 2011.

MATTIODA, F. ; BITTENCOURT, J. V. M. ; SANTOS JUNIOR, G. . Inovações na agricultura familiar: estudo de caso em propriedades rurais leiteiras no Paraná. In: XXXI Encontro Nacional de Engenharia de Produção, 2011, Belo Horizonte. XXXI Encontro Nacional de Engenharia de Produção, 2011.

MATTIODA, F. ; BITTENCOURT, J. V. M. . Qualidade do leite de pequenas propriedades rurais da Região Sudeste do Paraná.. In: XXX Encontro Nacional de Engenhar ia de Produção, 2010, São Carlos. XXX Encontro Nacional de Engenhar ia de Produção, 2010.

In: Food Science Research … Volume 1
Editor: Lucille Monaco Cacioppo

ISBN: 978-1-63117-932-7
© 2014 Nova Science Publishers, Inc.

Chapter 21

KAZUNORI NANRI

Affiliation: Department of Neurology, Tokyo Medical University Hachioji Medical Center

Contact Point: 1163, Tatemachi, Hachioji, Tokyo, 193-0998, Japan

Date of Birth: Sept. 19, 1959

Education: I graduated from Tokyo Medical University in 1985

Research and Professional Experience:

I received MD at Tokyo Medical University on studies with cerebral ischemia. From 1996 to 1997, I did research on the relationship between nitric oxide and cerebral ischemia in Centre National de la Recherche Scientifique, France. Since 2003, I have been engaged in clinical research on autoimmune cerebellar ataxia, and published important papers.

Professional Appointments:

I am Professor of Neurology of Tokyo Medical University Hachioji Medical Center. I am also an assistant director of Tokyo Medical University Hachioji Medical Center.

Publications Last 3 Years:

Nanri K, Niwa H, Mitoma H, Takei A, Ikeda J, Harada T, Okita M, Takeguchi M, Taguchi T, Mizusawa H. [Low-Titer Anti-GAD-Antibody-Positive Cerebellar Ataxia]_Cerebellum. 2012 Aug 26.

Tanaka N, Otake H, Ito S, Niiyama K, Nanri K. [A case of anti-TPO/gliadin antibody-positive cerebellar atrophy that responded to intravenous immunoglobulin therapy begun 16 years after onset]_Rinsho Shinkeigaku. 2012;52(5):351-5.

Nanri K, Shibuya M, Taguchi T, Hasegawa A, Tanaka N. [Selective loss of Purkinje cells in a patient with anti-gliadin-antibody-positive autoimmune cerebellar ataxia] Diagn Pathol. 2011 Feb 4;6:14.

Kobayashi M, Nanri K, Tanaka N, Hasegawa A, Taguchi T, Saito K. [A case of autoimmune polyglandular syndrome-related Parkinsonian syndrome that required differentiation from multiple system atrophy] Rinsho Shinkeigaku. 2010 Oct;50(10):704-9.

Saito H, Ohtsuka K, Takahashi H, Miura H, Taguchi T, Nanri K. [A case of lung adenocarcinoma presenting with chorea with bilateral basal ganglial lesions on MRI]. Rinsho Shinkeigaku. 2010 Aug;50(8):556-60.

Nanri K, Koizumi K, Mitoma H, Taguchi T, Takeguchi M, Ishiko T, Otsuka T, Nishioka H, Mizusawa H. [Classification of cerebellar atrophy using voxel-based morphometry and SPECT with an easy Z-score imaging system] Intern Med. 2010;49(6):535-41. Epub 2010 Mar 15.

Ishiko T, Taguchi T, Takeguchi M, Saito H, Nanri K. [Case of Wernicke's encephalopathy and subacute combined degeneration of the spinal cord due to vitamin deficiency showing changes in the bilateral corpus striatum and cardiac arrest due to beriberi heart disease]. Brain Nerve. 2009 Sep;61(9):1069-73.

Nanri K, Okita M, Takeguchi M, Taguchi T, Ishiko T, Saito H, Otsuka T, Mitoma H, Koizumi K. [Intravenous immunoglobulin therapy for autoantibody-positive cerebellar ataxia] Intern Med. 2009;48(10):783-90. Epub 2009 May 15.

In: Food Science Research ... Volume 1
Editor: Lucille Monaco Cacioppo

ISBN: 978-1-63117-932-7
© 2014 Nova Science Publishers, Inc.

Chapter 22

OMWOMA SOLOMON

Affiliation: Maseno University

Contact Point: Department of Chemistry, Maseno University, P.O. Box 333-40105 Maseno, Kenya

Date of Birth: Aug. 1, 1979

Education: Ph.D. Environmental Chemistry

Research and Professional Experience: Effects and mitigation of chemical contaminants in the environment

Professional Appointments: Lecturer

Publications Last 3 Years:

Omwoma, Solomon, Joseph O. Lalah, David MK Ongeri, and Karl-Werner Schramm. "The impact of agronomic inputs on selected physicochemical features and their relationships with heavy metals levels in surface sediment and water in sugarcane farms in Nzoia, Kenya." *Environmental Earth Sciences*: 10.1007/s12665-013-2824-y

Omwoma, Solomon, Wei Chen, Ryo Tsunashima, and Yu-Fei Song. "Recent Advances on Polyoxometalates Intercalated Layered Double Hydroxides: From Synthetic Approaches to Functional Material Applications." *Coordination Chemistry Reviews*, 258–2559, 2014, 58–71.

Omwoma Solomon, Wesley N. Omwoyo, Joseck O. Alwala, David M.K. Ongeri, Lagat C. Sylus and Joseph O. Lalah, Nutrient Reduction in Runoff Water from Sugarcane Farms by Sedimentation Method. *Environmentalist* 32(4) 2012 494-502

Omwoma Solomon, 2012. *Environmental Impacts of Sugarcane Farming, Kenya: Effects of Nitrogenous Fertilizer use on Soil and Water Chemistry within the Sugarcane Farms.* LAP Lambert Academic Publishing, Germany.

Omwoma Solomon, Joseph O. Lalah, David M. K. Ongeri and Maurice B. Wanyonyi, (2010). Impact of Fertilizers on Heavy Metal Loads in Surface Soils in Nzoia Nucleus Estate Sugarcane Farms in Western Kenya. *Bull. Environ. Contam. Toxicol.* 85(6):602-8.

In: Food Science Research ... Volume 1
Editor: Lucille Monaco Cacioppo

ISBN: 978-1-63117-932-7
© 2014 Nova Science Publishers, Inc.

Chapter 23

ANEEZA SOOBADAR

Affiliation: Mauritius Sugarcane Industry Research Institute

Contact Point: Réduit, Mauritius

Date of Birth: 16th April 1973

Education:
> PhD – University of Avignon, France-2009
> MSc – University of Sussex, UK- 1996
> BSc - University of Mauritius, Mauritius- 1995

Research and Professional Experience:
> Fertilizer management in sugar cane with emphasis on N mineralisation in soil
> Organic wastes as nutrients for sugar cane
> Fate of pesticide residues in soils

Professional Appointments:
> Responsible for fertilizer management for sugarcane in Ivory Coast
> Member of Conformity Assessment Standards, Mauritius Standards Bureau, Mauritius

Publications Last 3 Years:

A.SOOBADAR and K.F. NG KEE KWONG. (2013). Impact of fertilization of sugarcane with high rates of vinasse on groundwater quality in Mauritius. *Proc. Int. Soc. Sugar Cane Technol.*, Vol. 28, 2013,11 pp.

A.SOOBADAR and K.F. NG KEE KWONG. (2012). Impact of high rates of vinasse on some pertinent soil characteristics and sugarcane yield in Mauritius. *Journal of Sustainable Agriculture*, 36: 36-53.

In: Food Science Research ... Volume 1
Editor: Lucille Monaco Cacioppo

ISBN: 978-1-63117-932-7
© 2014 Nova Science Publishers, Inc.

Chapter 24

GILVAN WOSIACKI

Affiliation: Universidade Estadual de Ponta Grossa

Contact Point: Rua Leopoldo Guimarães da Cunha 1551 CEP 84.035-310 Ponta Grossa
PR Brazil

Date of Birth: Apr. 17, 1947

Education: Biochemistry Engineering

Research and Professional Experience: Pectinology, enzymes, physical biochemistry
Apple Starch Functional juices

Publications Last 3 Years:

1. ALMEIDA, D. M.; PRESTES, R. A.; PINHEIRO, L. A.; WOICIECHOWSKI, A. L.;
    WOSIACKI, G. . Propriedades físicas, químicas e de barreira em biofilme formados por
    blenda de celulose bacteriana e fécula de batata. Polímeros (São Carlos. Impresso), v. 23,
    p. 1-9, 2013.
2. ROCHA, A. S.; ZIELINSKI, A. A. F.; AVILA, S.; NOGUEIRA, A.; WOSIACKI, G. .
    Influence of processing on the quality of pomaceas juice (Pyrus. Acta Scientiarum.
    Agronomy (Impresso), v. 35, p. 101-107, 2013.
3. LEMOS, LORENA RANUCCI; NOGUEIRA, A.; WOSIACKI, G.; LACERDA, LUIZ
    GUSTAVO; DEMIATE, Ivo Mottin . The Influence of Different Amounts of Dextran
    and Starch in Crystallized Sugar in the Formation of Floc in Acidic Carbonated Solutions
    and Alcoholic Solutions. Sugar Tech, v. 15, p. 65-70, 2013.
4. BRAGA, CÍNTIA MAIA; ZIELINSKI, ACÁCIO ANTONIO FERREIRA; SILVA,
    KAROLLINE MARQUES DA; SOUZA, FREDERICO KOCH FERNANDES DE;
    PIETROWSKI, GIOVANA DE ARRUDA MOURA; COUTO, MARCELO;

GRANATO, DANIEL; Wosiacki, Gilvan; NOGUEIRA, Alessandro . Classification of Juices and Fermented Beverages Made From Unripe, Ripe and Senescent Apples Based on the Aromatic Profile Using Chemometrics. Food Chemistry, v. 141, p. 967-974, 2013.

5. ALMEIDA, DENISE MILLEO; PRESTES, Rosilene Aparecida; FONSECA, ADRIEL FERREIRA DA; WOICIECHOWSKI, ADENISE L.; Wosiacki, Gilvan . Minerals consumption by Acetobacter xylinum on cultivation medium on coconut water. Brazilian Journal of Microbiology (Impresso), v. 44, p. 197-206, 2013.

6. GABRIEL, LUCIANA SUTIL; PRESTES, Rosilene Aparecida; PINHEIRO, LUÍS ANTONIO; BARISON, ANDERSSON; Wosiacki, Gilvan . Multivariate analysis of the spectroscopic profile of the sugar fraction of apple pomace. Brazilian Archives of Biology and Technology (Impresso), v. 56, p. 439-446, 2013.

7. Ávila,S.; ZIELINSKI, A. A. F.; GOLTZ, C.; NOGUEIRA, Alessandro; Wosiacki, Gilvan . Malpighia glabra L. Evolution of the chromatic and antioxidant parameters in thre differents stages of acerola ripening.. Fruit Processing, v. 23, p. 222-227, 2013.

8. ZIELINSKI, A. A. F.; Staron, E.; Rebelato, F.C.A.; NOGUEIRA, A.; WOSIACKI, G. . Blueberry extract to enhance the antioxidant potential or apple juice. Fruit Processing, v. 22, p. 94-99, 2012.

9. PRESTES, R. A.; ALMEIDA, D. M.; BARISON, A.; PINHEIRO, L. A.; WOSIACKI, G. . Caracterização por ressonância magnética nuclear de sucos de maçã obtidos por preparações enzimáticas. Química Nova (Impresso), v. 35, p. 1141-1145, 2012.

10. BARBOSA, R.; GRANERO, J. C.; ALMEIDA, M. M.; PINHEIRO, L. A.; SAUER, E.; Wosiacki, Gilvan; PRESTES, R. A. . PERFIL ESPECTROSCÓPICO E CROMATOGRÁFICO DO ÓLEO DA MAÇÃ FUJI E GALA. Revista Brasileira de Tecnologia Agroindustrial, v. 6, p. n. 01/p. 630-639, 2012.

11. CANTERI, Maria Helene; WOSIACKI, G.; MORENO, LIRIAN; SCHEER, AGNES DE P. . Pectina: da matéria-prima ao produto final. Polímeros (São Carlos. Impresso), v. 22, p. 149-157, 2012.

12. DE ARRUDA MOURA PIETROWSKI, GIOVANA; DOS SANTOS, CAROLINE MONGRUEL ELEUTÉRIO; SAUER, Elenise; Wosiacki, Gilvan; NOGUEIRA, Alessandro . Influence of Fermentation with Hanseniaspora sp. Yeast on the Volatile Profile of Fermented Apple. Journal of Agricultural and Food Chemistry, v. 60, p. 9815-9821, 2012.
Citações:1

13. Canteri, M.H.G.; Scheer, A.P.; GINIES, C.; Reich, M.; RENARD, C.M.C.G.; WOSIACKI, G. . RHEOLOGICAL AND MACROMOLECULAR QUALITY OF PECTIN EXTRACTED WITH NITRIC ACID FROM PASSION FRUIT RIND. Journal of Food Process Engineering, v. 35, p. 800-809, 2012.

14. DE SOUZA NEVES ELLENDERSEN, LUCIANA; GRANATO, DANIEL; BIGETTI GUERGOLETTO, KARLA; Wosiacki, Gilvan . Development and sensory profile of a probiotic beverage from apple fermented with Lactobacillus casei. Engineering in Life Sciences (Print), v. 12, p. 475-485, 2012.

15. ZIELINSKI, A. A. F.; GONGRA, M. T.; HOFFMANN, J.; NOGUEIRA, A.; WOSIACKI, G. . Sucrose-free fruit juices. Fruit Processing, v. 6, p. 210-215, 2012.

16. GRANERO, J. C.; BARBOSA, R.; ALMEIDA, D. M.; PINHEIRO, L. A.; WOSIACKI, G.; SAUER, E.; PRESTES, R. A. . Mudanças no perfil do bagaço de maçã tratado com

enzimas industriais. Revista Brasileira de Tecnologia Agroindustrial, v. 6, p. 874-875, 2012.

17. CARVALHO, José Ricardo; Marques da SILVA, Karolline; Maia BRAGA, Cíntia; ALBERTI, Aline; Wosiacki, Gilvan; NOGUEIRA, Alessandro . Efeito da clarificação com gelatina no teor de compostos fenólicos e na atividade antioxidante de fermentados de maçãs. Brazilian Journal of Food Technology (Online), v. 14, p. 41-49, 2011.

18. ALBERTI, Aline; VIEIRA, Renato Giovanetti; DRILLEAU, Jean Francoise; WOSIACKI, G.; NOGUEIRA, A. . Apple Wine Processing with Different Nitrogen Contents. Brazilian Archives of Biology and Technology (Impresso), v. 54, p. 551-558, 2011.

19. Geus, L.M.M.; LIMA, Regina Cristina Aparecida de; NOGUEIRA, Melissa Koch F. S.; NOGUEIRA, A.; WOSIACKI, G. . Nespera - Potential for a small fruit. Fruit Processing, v. 21, p. 101-111, 2011.

20. CHIQUETTO, Nelci Catarina; Silva SIMÕES, Deise Rosana; Wosiacki, Gilvan . Análise descritiva quantitativa de sidra com teor alcoólico diminuído. Brazilian Journal of Food Technology (Online), v. 14, p. 19-28, 2011.

21. Estefânea B Zortéa, Manoela; Mottin Demiate, Ivo; Aurélio Praxedes, Marco; Wosiacki, Gilvan . AVALIAÇÃO DA VISCOSIDADE APARENTE DE PASTAS DE AMIDOS NOS VISCOSÍMETROS BROOKFIELD RVDV-II+ PRO E RÁPIDO VISCO-ANALISADOR RVA-4. Revista Brasileira de Tecnologia Agroindustrial, v. 5, p. 326-335, 2011.

22. Almeida, D.M.; PRESTES, R. A.; DENARDI, Frederico; ZARDO, Danianni Marinho; VIEIRA, Renato Giovanetti; WOSIACKI, G. . COMPARACÃ O DOS PRINCIPIOS TECNOLÃ GICOS DO PROCESSAMENTO DE SUCO DE MAÃ Ã AOS DOS DE PÃ RA. Revista Brasileira de Tecnologia Agroindustrial, v. 5, p. 593-605, 2011.

23. Almeida, D.M.; PRESTES, R. A.; WOICIECHOWSKI, A. L.; Wosiacki, Gilvan . Application of Bacterial Cellulose Conserv Ation of Minimaly Processed Fruits. Revista Brasileira de Tecnologia Agroindustrial, v. 5, p. 356-366, 2011.

24. VIEIRA, Renato Giovanetti; PRESTES, R.; DENARDI, Frederico; NOGUEIRA, A.; WOSIACKI, G. . A chemical pattern brazilian apples. A chemometric approach based on the Fuji and Gala varieties. Ciência e Tecnologia de Alimentos (Impresso), v. 31, p. 418-426, 2011.

25. QUAST, E.; ALBERTI, A.; QUAST, L. B.; WOSIACKI, G.; NOGUEIRA, A.; SCHIMIDT, F. L. . Prunus mume - Fruit characteristics and the influence of different obtaining forms of Prunus mume extracts over total phenolic content and antioxidant capacity. Fruit Processing, v. 21, p. 238-241, 2011.

26. LOPES, T. P.; AVILA, S.; ZIELINSKI, A. A. F.; NOGUEIRA, A.; WOSIACKI, G. . TECHNOLOGICAL PRINCIPLES OF APPLE JUICE PROCESSING AS COMPARED TO THOSE OF PEAR. Revista Brasileira de Tecnologia Agroindustrial, v. 5, p. 593-605, 2011.

27. Carvalho, C.V.; CHIQUETTO, N.C.; WOSIACKI, G. . Foresight of physical-chemical characteristics of apple juice blends appointed to sparkling drink elaboration. Ciência e Tecnologia de Alimentos (Impresso), v. 31, p. jan.-mar.2011, 2011.

28. SOUZA, F. K. F.; DA LUZ, R. O.; DOS SANTOS, C. E. M.; PIETROWSKI, G. A. M.; WOSIACKI, G.; NOGUEIRA, A. . Development of fermentator in series for the study of

kinetic apple fermented. Revista Brasileira de Tecnologia Agroindustrial, v. 5, p. 379-386, 2011.

29. Sato, Mariana Fátima; RIGONI, Dayane; CANTERI, M.H.G.; ZARDO, Danianni Marinho; PETKOWICZ, Carmem Lúcia de Oliveira; NOGUEIRA, Alessando; Wosiacki, Gilvan . Chemical and instrumental characterization of pectin from dried pomace of eleven apple cultivars. Acta Scientiarum. Agronomy (Impresso), v. 33, p. 383-389, 2011.

30. Sato, Mariana Fátima; RIGONI, Dayane; CANTERI, M.H.G.; ZARDO, Danianni Marinho; PETKOWICZ, Carmem Lúcia de Oliveira; Wosiacki, Gilvan; WOSIACKI, G. . Chemical and instrumental characterization of pectin from dried pomace of eleven apple cultivars. Acta Scientiarum. Agronomy (Impresso), v. 33, p. 383-389, 2011.

31. Queji, M.D.; WOSIACKI, G.; Cordeiro, G, A.; Peralta-Zamora, P.G.; NAGATA, Noemi . Determination of the simple sugars, malic acid and total phenolic compounds in apple pomace by infrared spectroscopy and PLSR. International Journal of Food Science & Technology (Print), v. 49, p. 602-609, 2010.

32. Canteri, Maria H. G.; Scheer, Agnes P.; WOSIACKI, G.; Ginies, Christian; Reich, Marise; Renard, Catherine M. C. G. . A Comparative Study of Pectin Extracted from Passion Fruit Rind Flours. Journal of Polymers and the Environment, p. .-., 2010.

33. Canteri,M.H.G.; SCHEER, A.; PETKOWICZ, Carmem Lúcia de Oliveira; Ginies, C; RENARD, Catherine; Wosiacki, Gilvan . Physicochemical composition ofthe yellowpassion fruit pericar fractions and respective pectic substances. Journal of Food and Nutrition Research, v. 49, p. 113-122, 2010.

34. Carvalho, J. R. F.; Silva, K.M.; SIMÕES, Deise Rosana Silva; NOGUEIRA, A.; WOSIACKI, G. . Elaboração de um fermentado frisante de maçã com características semelhantes às da sidra francesa. Boletim do Centro de Pesquisa e Processamento de Alimentos (Impresso), v. 28, p. 97-114, 2010.

35. Canteri, M.H.G.; SCHEER, Agnes de Paula; Ginnies, C.; RENARD, Catherine C C M; WOSIACKI, G. . IMPORTÃ NCIA DO TRATAMENTO TÃ RMICO NA CASCA DE MARACUJÃ PARA EXTRAÃ Ã O DE PECTINA. Revista Brasileira de Tecnologia Agroindustrial, v. 4, p. 109-121, 2010.

36. COELHO, Laylla Marques; Wosiacki, Gilvan . Avaliação sensorial de produtos panificados com adição de farinha de bagaço de maçã. Ciência e Tecnologia de Alimentos (Impresso), v. 30, p. 582-588, 2010.

37. CHIQUETTO, N.C.; WOSIACKI, G.; SIMOES, D. R. S. . Análise descritiva quantitativa de sidra com teor alcoólico diminuído. Brazilian Journal of Food Technology (Online), v. 6 sen, p. 19-28, 2010.

38. Wosiacki, Gilvan; NOGUEIRA, Melissa Koch F. S.; NOGUEIRA, A.; Kintopp, S.E.; Botelho, V.M.B.; VIEIRA, Renato Giovanetti . Functional Fruits in the Araucaria Forest/ Brasil. Fruit Processing, v. 20, p. 118-122, 2010.

39. Wosiacki, Gilvan; Sato, Mariana Fátima; VIEIRA, Renato Giovanetti; ZARDO, Danianni Marinho; Falcão, Leila Denise; NOGUEIRA, Alessandro . Apple pomace from eleven cultivars: an approach to identify sources of bioactive compounds. Acta Scientiarum. Agronomy (Online), v. 32, p. 29-35, 2010.

Book: Ellendersen,L.S.N.; WOSIACKI, G. . Análise Sensorial Descritiva Quantitativa. 1. ed. Ponta Grossa: Editora da Universidade Estadual de Ponta Grossa, 2010. v. 1. 89p .

Book chapter:

Giovanetti Canteri, Maria Helene; NOGUEIRA, Alessandro; Oliveira Petkowicz, Carmen Lucia de; Wosiacki, Gilvan . Characterization of Apple Pectin A Chromatographic Approach. In: Leonardo de Azevedo Calderon. (Org.). Characterization of Apple Pectin - - A chromatographic approach. 1aed.Zagreb: InTech, 2012, v. , p. 325-342.

NOGUEIRA, A.; WOSIACKI, G. . Apple cider fermentation.. In: Y. H. Hui; E. Özgül Evranuz. (Org.). Handbook of Plant-Based Fermented Food and Beverage Technology. Handbook of Plant-Based Fermented Food and Beverage Technology.. 2eded.New York: CRC Press Taylor & Francis Group, 2012, v. , p. 209-232.

Wosiacki, Gilvan; NOGUEIRA, Alessandro . Suco de maçã. In: Waldemar Venturini. (Org.). Bebidas não alcoõlicas. 2ed.São Paulo: Edgard Blücher, 2010, v. 1, p. 269-302.

NOGUEIRA, Alesandro; WOSIACKI, G. . Sidra. In: WaldemarGastoni Venturini. (Org.). Bebidas Alcoólicas Ciência e Tecnologia v. 2. 1 ed.São Paulo: Edgard Blücher, 2010, v. 1, p. 113-142.

In: Food Science Research ... Volume 1
Editor: Lucille Monaco Cacioppo

ISBN: 978-1-63117-932-7
© 2014 Nova Science Publishers, Inc.

Chapter 25

SLAĐANA M. ŽILIĆ

Affiliation: Maize Research Institute, Department of Technology, Belgrade, Serbia

Contact Point: Slobodana Bajica 1, 11085 Belgrade

Date of Birth: May 19, 1969

Education:
-2011 Postdoctoral study, Hacettepe University, Food Engineering Department, Ankara, Turkey
-1999-2004 PhD, University of Belgrade, Faculty of Agriculture, Department of Food Technology and Biochemistry
-1993/1994 - 1996/1997 MSc, University of Belgrade, Faculty of Agriculture
-1988/1989 – 1993 BSc, University of Belgrade, Faculty of Agriculture

Research and Professional Experience: Employed in Maize Research Institute from 1993.

Research topic of interest: proteins, bioactive compounds (fenolic compounds, carotenoids, Maillard reaction products), processing contaminants (Maillard reaction), chemical changes occurring in foods during processing with a focus on quality and safety, grain quality.

Professional Appointments:

2004-2009	Head of Technology Department, Maize Research Institute
2006-	Member of the Scientific Council, Maize Research Institute
2011-	Manager of National Project
2012-	Member of International Maillard Reaction Society
2011-	Member of the Serbian Association of Food Technologists

Publications Last 3 Years:

Barać Miroljub, Čabrilo Slavica, Pesic Mirjana, Stanojević Sladjana, *Žilic Slađana*, Ognjen Maćej, Ristić Nikola, (2010). Profile and technological-functional properties of proteins from six pea (Pisum sativum) genotypes. International Journal of Molecular Sciences, 11, (12) 4973-4990.

Slađana Žilić, Dejan Dodig, Vesna Hadži-Tašković Šukalović, Milan Maksimović, Goran Saratlić, Biljana Škrbić (2010). Bread and durum wheat compared for antioxidants contents, and lipoxygenase and peroxidase activities. International Journal of Food Science and Technology. 45, 7, 1360-1366.

Žilić Slađana, Vesna Hadži-Tašković Šukalović, Marija Milašinović, Dragana Ignjatović-Micić, Milan Maksimović, Valentina Semenčenko (2010): Effect of micronisation on the composition and properties of the flour from white, yellow and red maize. Food Technology and Biotechnology. 48, 2, 198-206.

Slađana Žilić, Miroljub Barać, Mirjana Pešić, Dragana Ignjatović-Micić, Mirjana Srebrić, Snežana Mladenović Drinić, (2011). Characterization of proteins from kernel of different soybean varieties. Journal of Science of Food and Agriculture 91, 60-67.

Slađana Žilić, Vesna Hadži-Tašković Šukalović, Dejan Dodig, Vuk Maksimović, Milan Maksimović, Zorica Basić (2011). Antioxidant activity of small grain cereals caused by phenolics and lipid soluble antioxidants. Journal of Cereal Science, 54, 3 417-424.

Slađana Žilić, Miroljub Barać, Mirjana Pešić, Dejan Dodig, Dragana Ignjatović-Micić (2011). Characterization of proteins from grain of different bread and durum wheat genotypes. International Journal of Molecular Science, 12, 5878-5894.

Slađana Žilić, Marija Milašinović, Dušanka Terzić, Miroljub Barać, Dragana Ignjatović Micić 2011. Grain characteristics and composition of maize specialty hybrids. Spanish Journal of Agricultural Research. 9, 1, 230-241.

Slađana Žilić, Dejan Dodig, Marija Milašinović Šeremešić, Vesna Kandić, Marija Konstadinović, Slaven Prodanović and Đorđe Savić (2011). Small grain cereals compared for dietary fibre and protein contents. Genetika 43, 2, 381-396.

Slađana Žilić, Miroljub Barać, Mirjana Pešić, Vesna Hadži-Tašković Šukalović, Dejan Dodig, Snežana Mladenović Drinić, Marijana Janković (2011). Genetic variability of albumin-globulin content, and lipoxygenase, peroxidase activities among bread and durum wheat genotypes. Genetika, 43, 3, 503-516.

Slađana Žilić, Arda Serpen, Gül Akıllıoğlu, Vural Gökmen, Jelena Vančetović (2012). Phenolic compounds, carotenoids, anthocyanins and antioxidant capacity of colored maize (*Zea mays* L.) kernels. Journal of Agricultural and Food Chemistry. 60 (5), 1224-1231.

Slađana Žilić, Arda Serpen, Gül Akıllıoğlu, Marijana Janković, Vural Gökmen (2012). Distributions of phenolic compounds, yellow pigments and oxidative enzymes in wheat grains and their relation to antioxidant capacity of bran and debranned flour. Journal of Cereal Science. DOI: 10.1016/j.jcs.2012.07.014

Slađana Žilić, Gül Akıllıoğlu, Arda Serpen, Miroljub Barać, Vural Gökmen (2012). Effects of isolation, enzymatic hydrolysis, heating, hydratation and Maillard reaction on the antioxidant capacity of cereal and legume proteins. Food Research International 49, 1-8.

Denić M., Ignjatović Micić D., Stankovic G., Marković K., *Žilić S.,* Lazić Jančić V., Chauque P, Fato P., Senete C., Mariote D. and Haag W. (2012). Role of genetic resources from different gegraphic and climatic regions in simultaneous breeding for high quality protein maize (hqpm) and stress tolerance. Genetika, 44, 1, 13-23.

In: Food Science Research ... Volume 1
Editor: Lucille Monaco Cacioppo

ISBN: 978-1-63117-932-7
© 2014 Nova Science Publishers, Inc.

Chapter 26

RENATA PUPPIN ZANDONADI

Affiliation: University of Brasilia

Contact Point: Departamento de Nutrição, Universidade de Brasília, Campus Universitário Darcy Ribeiro, Asa Norte, Brasília, Brazil, 70910-900. E-mail: renatapz@yahoo.com.br - Phone number: +55-61-31071778

Date of Birth: 07/05/1982

Education:
Ph.D., Health Sciences, University of Brasilia, 2009
MSc., Human Nutrition, University of Brasilia, 2006
Gr., Nutrition, University of Brasilia, 2003

Research and Professional Experience:
Research Group in Nutritional and Nourishment Quality, Department of Nutrition, University of Brasilia, Brasilia, DF, 70910-900, Brazil

Professional Appointments:
Associate Professor, Department of Nutrition, University of Brasilia, 2009-present.
Associate Professor, Department of Nutrition, Unieuro, 2004-2009.
Substitute Professor, Department of Nutrition, University of Brasilia, 2004-2006.

Publications Last 3 Years:

Laporte L, Zandonadi RP. Chefs' knowledgement about coeliac disease. Alimentos e Nutrição. 2012;22:465-470.

Zandonadi RP, Botelho RA, Gandolfi L, Ginani JS, Montenegro F, Pratesi R. Green banana pasta: an alternative for gluten-free diets. Journal of the American Dietetic Association. 2012;112:1068-1072.

Vieira AR, Dias AR, Cunha AGF, Hargreaves SM, Santos SGS, Botelho RBA, Zandonadi RP. Massa de empada sem glúten e sem leite, enriquecida com biomassa de banana verde. Nutrição Brasil. 2011;10:175-178.

Araújo HMC, Araújo WMC, Botelho RBA, Zandonadi RP. Celiac disease, eating habits and practices and life quality of life. Revista de Nutrição. 2010;23:467-474.

Ginani VC, Ginani JS, Botelho RBA, Zandonadi RP, Akutsu RC, Araujo WMC. Reducing fat content of brazilian traditional preparations does not alter food acceptance: development of a model for fat reduction that conciliates health and culture. Journal of Culinary Science & Technology. 2010;8:229-241.

Zandonadi RP. Glúten e individualidade bioquímica. Brazilian Journal of Functional Nutrition. 2010;11:54-60.

Zandonadi RP, Botelho RA. Macarrão sem glúten (com psyllium). Brazilian Journal of Functional Nutrition. 2010;11:62-62.

Cunha JG, Oliveira PSG, Mendes TG, Ginani JS, Zandonadi RP. Efeitos dos diferentes tipos de processadores domésticos na produção de suco de frutas e seu impacto na curva glicêmica. Alimentos e Nutrição. 2010;21:63-68.

Felinto VT, Almeida RC, Paiva AL, Garcez N, Zandonadi RP. Análise da rotulagem de chocolates quanto à presença de glúten. Higiene Alimentar. 2010;24:182-186.

Teixeira AP, Melo GR, Zandonadi RP. Aceitação e percepção dos estudantes de gastronomia e nutrição em relação aos alimentos funcionais. Alimentos e Nutrição. 2010;21:367-372.

Zandonadi RP, Botelho RA, Araújo WMC. Psyllium as a substitute for gluten in bread. Journal of the American Dietetic Association. 2009;109:1781-1784.

Zandonadi RP, Resende AJ, Teixeira AP, Paiva CF. O efeito da adição de batata yacon no suco de laranja industrializado na curva glicêmica de estudantes universitários. Alimentos e Nutrição. 2009;20:313-319.

PART II

RESEARCH SUMMARIES

In: Food Science Research ... Volume 1
Editor: Lucille Monaco Cacioppo

ISBN: 978-1-63117-932-7
© 2014 Nova Science Publishers, Inc.

Chapter 27

SICKLY SWEET: SUGAR, REFINED CARBOHYDRATE, ADDICTION AND GLOBAL OBESITY

Simon Thornley
University of Auckland
Hayden McRobbie
Queen Mary University of London, London, UK

RESEARCH SUMMARY

Is there evidence for addiction to food? How strong is this evidence? If so, what element of food makes it addictive? Over the last forty years, our waistlines have continued to expand in nearly all countries, despite attempts to slim populations. Does this information shed any light on the seemingly insoluble obesity epidemic? This book explores a radical rethink in what has caused the global obesity epidemic. A consideration of which types of food are most likely to be responsible is presented, as well as an understanding of how human motivation and addiction may help us understand why people gain weight. Parallels with a range of other addiction syndromes to help uncover the elusive key to unlocking the obesity epidemic are considered.

In: Food Science Research ... Volume 1
Editor: Lucille Monaco Cacioppo

ISBN: 978-1-63117-932-7
© 2014 Nova Science Publishers, Inc.

Chapter 28

FOOD CHEMISTRY

Dongfeng Wang
Qingdao, P. R. China
Hong Lin
Ocean University of China, P. R. China
Jianqian Kan
Southwest University, P. R. China
Linwei Liu
Northwest A&F University, Yangling, ShaanXi, China
Xiaoxing Zeng
Nanjing Agricultural University, China
Shengrong Shen
Zhejiang University, China

RESEARCH SUMMARY

This book introduces the chemistry and properties of six essential nutrients contained in foods, including water, carbohydrates, lipids, proteins, vitamins, and minerals and special attention is given to their changes undergone during processing and storage and the effects of these changes on the quality of foods. Food additives and toxic substances in foods are also included in this book. Tables and illustrations will be widely employed in the book to offer readers with in-depth insight into food chemistry. These features make the book a valuable tool for food chemists, food technologists, engineers, biochemists, nutritionists, and analytical chemists for food and agricultural research, food control and other related purposes. The book can also be used as a textbook for university students and teachers for learning and teaching Food Chemistry.

In: Food Science Research ... Volume 1
Editor: Lucille Monaco Cacioppo
ISBN: 978-1-63117-932-7
© 2014 Nova Science Publishers, Inc.

Chapter 29

OILS AND FATS FOR THE FUTURE. A CASE STUDY: SAFOU (DACRYODES EDULIS) FROM THE CONGO BASIN COUNTRIES IN AFRICA

Thomas Silou

University of Brazzaville, Congo, Africa

RESEARCH SUMMARY

In the last ten years the production and consumption of the safou, the fruit of Dacryodes edulis (Burseracées) have seen a remarkable growth in central Africa. In 1980 a network was set up dedicated essentially to the commercial development of the safou, called the African Safou Network (ASANET). Its commercialisation has spread beyond national boundaries, and has become international throughout the sub-region. All this activity has allowed significant advances in physical, chemical and biological knowledge concerning this plant and its fruit

In: Food Science Research … Volume 1
Editor: Lucille Monaco Cacioppo

ISBN: 978-1-63117-932-7
© 2014 Nova Science Publishers, Inc.

Chapter 30

METABOLIC ASPECTS OF MACRONUTRIENTS

Mostafa I. Waly, MPH, MSc, PhD
Department of Food Science and Nutrition, CAMS,
Sultan Qaboos University, Muscat, Oman

RESEARCH SUMMARY

This book is designed and formatted for an undergraduate student level and fits with the curriculum of biochemistry courses in all medical universities throughout the world. This book represents educational material which will provide students with a simple understanding of basic concepts of the macronutrient metabolism, biochemical events of macronutrients inside human cells, and cellular regulation of different metabolic pathways. This textbook provides insight into the nutritional biochemistry of macronutrients (carbohydrates, fat and protein) and their metabolic fate. The book covers basic concepts of digestion and absorption of three essential nutrients and their utilization by human cells in anabolic and catabolic pathways. The book is designed to link basic biochemistry to metabolism with a specific reference to the enzymatic, hormonal regulation and integrated metabolic pathways.

Special attention was given to the central role of glucose in controlling energy production and its relevance to enzyme activation and inhibition. The major pathways that regulate carbohydrates, fat and protein metabolites in different organs are discussed in correlation to the metabolic fate of each nutrient and the cellular responses to different hormones. The book provides a thorough understanding and lays the foundation for the metabolic basis of macronutrients and the biochemistry underlying disease pathogenesis. Finally, the main theme of this book is to address the macronutrient metabolism in terms of anabolic, catabolic and amphibolic pathways.

In: Food Science Research ... Volume 1
Editor: Lucille Monaco Cacioppo

ISBN: 978-1-63117-932-7
© 2014 Nova Science Publishers, Inc.

Chapter 31

RESOURCES, CULTIVATION, CHEMISTRY AND BIOLOGICAL ACTIVITIES OF SALVIA MILTIORRHIZA

Chun Guang Li, Shujun Sheng and Brian May*

Traditional & Complementary Medicine Program,
RMIT Health Innovations Research Institute,
School of Health Sciences, RMIT University,
Bundoora, Victoria, Australia

RESEARCH SUMMARY

Salvia miltiorrhiza is a commonly used medicinal herb for treating cardiovascular and cerebrovascular diseases. It has diverse botanic and geographic origins in the herbal market. The quality of *Salvia miltiorrhiza* depends on the germplasm resources and the environmental and agricultural conditions under which it is grown. Various constituents with demonstrated biological activity have been identified from this herb. This article reviews the resources, cultivation, chemistry and biological activities of *Salvia miltiorrhiza*, in particular, its cultivation and medicinal applications.

* Corresponding Author. Tel.: +61 3 9925 7635; fax: +61 3 9925 7178. E-mail address: chun.guang.li@rmit.edu.au.

In: Food Science Research … Volume 1
Editor: Lucille Monaco Cacioppo

ISBN: 978-1-63117-932-7
© 2014 Nova Science Publishers, Inc.

Chapter 32

CUNILA D. ROYEN EX. L., GLECHON EPL. AND HESPEROZYGIS EPL. (LAMIACEAE) IN SOUTH AMERICA: AN ETHNOBOTANICAL AND PHYTOCHEMICAL REVIEW

G. Agostini[*,1], T. S. Ribeiro[2], S. Moura[2], S. Echeverrigaray[2] and T. T. Souza-Chies[1]

[1]Programa de Pós-Graduação em Botânica, Departamento de Botânica, Bento Gonçalves,
Universidade Federal do Rio Grande do Sul,
Porto Alegre, RS, Brazil
[2]Instituto de Biotecnologia, Universidade de Caxias do Sul,
Universidade de Caxias do Sul. R. Francisco Getúlio Vargas,
Caxias do Sul, RS, Brazil

RESEARCH SUMMARY

The genera *Cunila*, *Glechon* and *Hesperozygis* have been addressed in studies regarding natural products in the last two decades. Several native species are used in South American folk medicine justifying the scientific surveys and earning increasing attention from pharmacological and cosmetic industries among others. The growing research on native plants has discovered an excellent source of useful chemical compounds promising for several industries. Along with the increasing scope of chemical researches, concerns about the maintenance of natural populations and its genetic variability have raised. The current chapter encompasses an actual review about essential oils from South America native plants with potential aromatic and medicinal uses.

[*] Corresponding Author: E-mail: sabonim.radan@gmail.com, Tel.: 55 51 3308-7578, Fax: 55 51 3308-7755.

In: Food Science Research ... Volume 1
Editor: Lucille Monaco Cacioppo

ISBN: 978-1-63117-932-7
© 2014 Nova Science Publishers, Inc.

Chapter 33

CULTIVATION OF AROMATIC PLANTS UNDER IRRIGATION WITH SECONDARY-TREATED EFFLUENT

N. Bernstein[1], D. Chaimovitch[2] and N. Dudai[2]

[1]Institute of Soil Water and Environmental Sciences,
Volcai Center, Bet-Dagan, Israel
[2]Aromatic, Medicinal and Spice Crops, ARO,
Newe Ya'ar Research Center, Ramat Yishay, Israel

RESEARCH SUMMARY

Perennial aromatic plants are cultivated as cash-crops for fresh or dry herb production, or as a source of essential oils. They require substantial amounts of water in order to satisfy their potential for intensive production. In arid and semiarid regions, where shortage of fresh-water restricts agricultural production, irrigation with marginal water is an unavoidable practice. The largest source of marginal water for agriculture is secondary-treated municipal sewage water. This water differs chemically and physically from the potable water from which they originated, and may therefore affect the irrigated plants. Development of aromatic production systems based on irrigation with treated effluent, will allow development of essential oil production systems in arid and semi-arid zones. In the present study we have screened a range of aromatic crops for their suitability to grow under irrigation with secondary treated effluent, and as a source of essential oil. During a three years project, the growth and morphological development of six aromatic plants, and their yield quantity and quality under irrigation with effluent, was compared to cultivation with potable water. The results which demonstrate that secondary treated municipal effluent are suitable for growth and quality production in all species tested, forms the foundation for effluent-based industrial essential oil production.

In: Food Science Research … Volume 1
Editor: Lucille Monaco Cacioppo

ISBN: 978-1-63117-932-7
© 2014 Nova Science Publishers, Inc.

Chapter 34

IMMUNOMODULATORY EFFECTS OF AYURVEDIC HERBS: MACROPHAGE ACTIVATION AND CYTOKINE SECRETION

Upadhyaya Smitha, Telkar Asha,
Bhat Jyoti and Banerjee Gautam[*]

Unilever R&D India, Whitefield, Bangalore, India

RESEARCH SUMMARY

Immunity or immune health is one of the main aspects of overall health of an individual. Indian traditional medicine or Ayurveda offers a wide range of beneficial herbs for human health and an array of herbs have been used to balance immunity status of an individual. The precise role of these herbs on immune health in the modern scientific context has not been investigated in detail.

This paper aims to elucidate the effect of few selected herbs i.e. *Withania somnifera, Ellettaria cardamomum, Ricinus communis, Zingiber officinalis, Trichopus zeylanicus, Glycyrrhiza glabra, Convolvulus pluricalis, Asparagus racemosus* and *Ipomoea digitata* on macrophage activation and pro/ anti- inflammatory cytokines release *in vitro*.

The ability of the above listed herbs on macrophage activation *in vitro* was tested using the murine cell line Raw 264.7. In addition to this, the ability of these herbs to release cytokines (IL 1α, IL 4, IFNγ and TNFα) from whole blood culture was investigated.

The herbs investigated exhibited distinct immunity enhancement property *in vitro*. Our investigations to certain extent could provide scientific evidence to support the usage of these herbs for improvement of immune health.

[*] Corresponding Author: Gautam Banerjee, Unilever R&D India, No. 64, Main Road, Whitefield, Bangalore – 560066, India. Tel: +91-80-39831068. Fax: +91-80-28453086. E mail: gautam.banerjee@unilever.com.

In: Food Science Research ... Volume 1
Editor: Lucille Monaco Cacioppo

ISBN: 978-1-63117-932-7
© 2014 Nova Science Publishers, Inc.

Chapter 35

DEVELOPMENT AND APPLICATION OF A CERTIFIED REFERENCE MATERIAL: CADMIUM AND LEAD IN CHINESE MEDICINAL HERB (*HERBA DESMODII STYRACIFOLII*)

Yiu-chung Wong[*], Siu-kay Wong and Della W. M. Sin

Analytical and Advisory Services Division, Government Laboratory,
Homantin Government Offices, Ho Man Tin, Hong Kong, China

RESEARCH SUMMARY

The determination of chemical contaminants in herbs relies on the applied analytical methodologies, which in turn should undergo thorough validation to support the intended purposes of measurements. Certified reference materials (CRMs) play an important role in quality assurance for chemical analyses and in evaluating the degree of measurement accuracy with respect to the assigned system of reference. Considering the continuous increase of trade in herbal materials as well as the limited supply of herbal CRMs in the market, the present research study aimed to develop a CRM on cadmium and lead in a common Chinese medicinal herb, *Herba Desmodii Styracifolii*, and to use the candidate CRM as the test material in two regional and international inter-laboratory comparsions and a proficiency testing (PT) programme. The major objectives of the works are to promote the concept of metrological traceability and to improve the competence of the chemical testing sector at large in quantitative analysis of heavy metals in herbal matrices.

[*] Corresponding Author, Email: ycwong@govtlab.gov.hk.

In: Food Science Research … Volume 1
Editor: Lucille Monaco Cacioppo

ISBN: 978-1-63117-932-7
© 2014 Nova Science Publishers, Inc.

Chapter 36

EFFECTS OF MEDICINAL HERB SALVIA MILTIORRHIZA ON BONE CELL ACTIVITIES

Yanqi Yang[1], Lei Chai[2], Ding Zhang[3] and A. B. M. Rabie[1]

[1]Faculty of Dentistry, the University of Hong Kong
[2]School of Dentistry, University of Queensland, Brisbane, Australia
[3]Peking Union Medical College Hospital, China

RESEARCH SUMMARY

Medicinal herbs have always been considered a healthy source of life, and their therapeutic properties are used to treat various diseases with the advantage that the medicinal herbs are being 100% natural. Active ingredients from some commonly used medicinal herbs have been found to be osteoinductive which can induce bone formation[1,2]. Bone is a highly vascularised tissue. In order for it to maintain homeostasis and regeneration, the development of microvasculature and microcirculation is crucial[3], therefore, osteogenesis and angiogenesis are closely linked. Salvia Miltiorrhiza (SM), also known as red sage, Chinese sage, tan shen, or danshen, is a perennial plant in the genus Salvia, highly valued for its roots as a medicinal herb[4]. SM has been widely used in China and, to a lesser extent, in Japan, the United States, and other European countries for the treatment of cardiovascular and cerebrovascular diseases by improving perfusion of ischemic myocardium and enhancing blood circulation due to its function to enhance angiogenesis[5,6].

Because of the close relationship between angiogenesis and bone formation, attention has been drawn on SM's positive effects on osteogenesis. SM was found to prevent the osteoporosis systematically in rats in an *in vivo* study[7]. At localized skull defects in rats, new bone formation was shown when grafted with SM extract in collagen matrix compared to collagen matrix alone[8].

The beneficial effects of SM on treatment of bone diseases such as osteoporosis and on bone healing in fractures have been understood to result from its positive effects on angiogenesis. The increased new blood vessels allow mesenchymal cells to be recruited to the area and to differentiate into cells such as osteoblasts, which will take part in the bone remodeling process. Besides this, is it possible that SM has direct effects on osteoblasts and/or osteoclasts so that it contributes to bone remodeling? The present chapter will focus on the effects of SM on bone formation and bone resorption by discussing its direct effects on osteoblasts and osteoclasts.

In: Food Science Research ... Volume 1
Editor: Lucille Monaco Cacioppo

ISBN: 978-1-63117-932-7
© 2014 Nova Science Publishers, Inc.

Chapter 37

SORGHUM: AN ENIGMATIC GRAIN FOR CHICKEN-MEAT PRODUCTION

Peter H. Selle[*], Sonia Y. Liu and Aaron J. Cowieson
Poultry Research Foundation within the University of Sydney, Australia

RESEARCH SUMMARY

In Australia, if not other countries, sorghum is an enigmatic grain for chicken-meat production because the performance of broiler chickens on sorghum-based diets is considered to be either occasionally or routinely inferior to those offered wheat-based diets. This chapter considers a number of factors which may be contributing to this situation including pellet quality, protein quality, grain texture, particle size of sorghum following hammer-milling and conditioning temperatures at which sorghum-based diets are steam-pelleted. However, it is considered that the challenges posed by these factors can be addressed, at least partially, and the appropriate strategies are discussed. Our contention is that the fundamental problem with sorghum is that its energy density, most of which is derived from starch, is relatively poorly utilised by broiler chickens and the underlying reasons have not been clarified. Considerable attention has been paid to the possible limiting role of kafirin, the dominant protein fraction in sorghum, on starch gelatinisation and digestibility. However, other factors that may be impeding starch digestion include glutelin, the second protein fraction in sorghum, phytate, and phenolic compounds (including 'non-tannin' phenolics, ferulic acid and possibly condensed tannin). It is proposed that the identification of the relative importance of these factors on sorghum starch digestion is key to solving the conundrum that is sorghum grain in chicken-meat production.

[*] Corresponding author: peter.selle@sydney.edu.au.

In: Food Science Research ... Volume 1
Editor: Lucille Monaco Cacioppo

ISBN: 978-1-63117-932-7
© 2014 Nova Science Publishers, Inc.

Chapter 38

UNLOCKING THE POTENTIAL OF SORGHUM FOR DEVELOPMENT IN EAST AFRICA

Tom Martin[1], Moses Biruma[2], Johan Fogelqvist[1],
Patrick Okori[3] and Christina Dixelius[1]*

[1]Dept. Plant Biology and Forest Genetics, Uppsala Biocenter,
Swedish University of Agricultural Sciences &
Linnean Center for Plant Biology, Uppsala, Sweden
[2]National Agriculture Research Organization, Entebbe, Uganda
[3]Dept. of Agricultural Production, School of Agricultural Sciences,
College of Agricultural & Environmental Sciences,
Makerere University, Kampala, Uganda

RESEARCH SUMMARY

Sorghum domestication probably dates back to the advent of agriculture in sub-Saharan Africa ~10,000 years ago. Today, it is an established understanding that the Sub-Saharan and North East regions of Africa are the primary centers of sorghum diversity. On the African continent, sorghum is grown on 25 million hectares, which constitutes approximately 61% of the world total however African yields average only 0.85 t/ha compared with 4.5 t/ha in North America. The low productivity is associated with; traditional modes of production, low levels of technology adoption, low uptake of improved varieties and hybrid-seed technology, environmental factors such as unpredicted drought periods and other soil-edaphic constraints, institutional bottlenecks such as research capacity, information barriers, poor infrastructure, marketing hardships, and environmental stresses the major determinants of present sorghum production and yield losses. We have cloned resistance genes (NB-LRR type) to the disease inciting fungi Setosphaeria turcica (St genes) and Colletotrichum sublineolum (Cs genes) causing turcicum leaf blight and sorghum anthracnose, respectively, using a differential transcriptomic approach on Ugandan sorghum genotypes. Presently we are re-sequencing

* Corresponding author: Christina.Dixelius@slu.se.

different sorghum genotypes to enhance our understanding of sorghum speciation but more importantly to generate knowledge on additional traits of interest. Wild sorghum species can survive with less water uptake, resist more diseases and insect pests and are presently used to widening the genetic diversity in a pre-breeding initiative. Further, molecular markers are being developed for a genomic selection approach in order to facilitate and speed up the selection processes not least to meet the climate change and emergent food security constrains due to the rapid population growth.

In: Food Science Research ... Volume 1
Editor: Lucille Monaco Cacioppo

ISBN: 978-1-63117-932-7
© 2014 Nova Science Publishers, Inc.

Chapter 39

THE HEALTH BENEFITS OF SORGHUM GRAIN FOR POULTRY AND PIGS

M. Mabelebele[1,2] and P. A. Iji[2]

[1]School of Agricultural and Environmental Sciences,
University of Limpopo, South Africa
[2]School of Environmental and Rural Science,
University of New England, Australia

RESEARCH SUMMARY

Sorghum is the fifth most important grain crop after wheat, rice, maize and barley. Sorghum is cultivated for food and beverages for humans, and for feed and fodder for animals in America, Asia, Australia and Africa. Its crude protein content is higher than that of maize whereas its energy value is rated as high as that of maize. Sorghum tolerates poorer growing conditions than maize, so is more abundant in marginal regions, where it is used to feed humans and animals. Sorghum may confer some health benefits on consumers due to the nature of its carbohydrates but also the presence of other chemicals, which ordinarily are regarded as antinutrients in animal nutrition, e.g. polyphenols or tannins and polycosanols. When fed to humans, these factors may be beneficial. Tannins would reduce feed intake and digestive enzyme activities, to minimize weight gain while polycosanols, present in the waxy layer, are known to reduce the concentrations of low-density lipoproteins and improve cardiac function. Sorghum is also free from gluten and therefore useful for people suffering from coeliac disease. Some of these benefits are also noticeable in animals although could be negative to productivity. Sorghum is therefore not seen to be an ingredient for controlling animal health and its use as such has not received significant attention in animal nutrition. This chapter discusses the direct health benefits associated with feeding sorghum grains to poultry and pigs. It will also link changes in animal product quality to health benefits of the human consumer.

In: Food Science Research ... Volume 1
Editor: Lucille Monaco Cacioppo

ISBN: 978-1-63117-932-7
© 2014 Nova Science Publishers, Inc.

Chapter 40

FUNGAL ROOT ENDOPHYTES AS SORGHUM GROWTH PROMOTERS

A. B. M. Vaz[1,2,*], I. Sampedro[3,†] and J. A. Ocampo[3,‡]

[1]Research Laboratory in Microbiology (LAPEM), Biological Sciences Department,
Feira de Santana State University,
Feira de Santana, Bahia, Brazil
[2]Center for Excellence in Bioinformatics, Genomics and Computational Biology
Group. Centro de Pesquisas René Rachou
(CPqRR) – FIOCRUZ, Minas Gerais, Brazil
[3]Department of Microbiology, Estación Experimental
del Zaidín, C.S.I.C., Profesor Albareda, Granada, Spain

RESEARCH SUMMARY

Fungal endophytes are found in healthy plant tissues during at least one stage of their life cycle and do not cause any apparent symptoms of disease or negatively affect the host. These fungi have been isolated from all plants studied in natural ecosystems. They can induce many changes in the plant ecology, fitness and evolution and, thus, can influence whole plant communities. The Ascomycetous root fungal endophytes can be divided into two groups, the dark septate endophytes (DSE) and the fungi with hyaline and pale hyphae. Fungal endophyte colonization is important for the improvement of the ecological adaptability of the host, resulting in enhanced tolerance of both biotic and abiotic stresses. Another important group of endophytes are those that constitute arbuscular mycorrhizal (AM) symbiosis. AM symbiosis is very important for plant nutrient uptake and growth and for plant resistance to biotic and

[*] Corresponding author: Aline B. M. Vaz. 1. PPG Biotecnologia UEFS/Fiocruz-BA. Av. Transnordestina s.n, Novo Horizonte, 44.036-900, Feira de Santana, BA – Brasil. 2. Centro de Excelência em Bioinformática (CEBio), Fundação Oswaldo Cruz (FIOCRUZ), Rua Araguari 741, 30190-110 Belo Horizonte, MG, Brazil. E-mail: alinebmv@hotmail.com.
[†] I. Sampedro: Department of Microbiology, Estación Experimental del Zaidín, C.S.I.C., Profesor Albareda, 1, E-18008, Granada, Spain.
[‡] J. A. Ocampo: Department of Microbiology, Estación Experimental del Zaidín, C.S.I.C., Profesor Albareda, 1, E-18008, Granada, Spain. E-mail: juanantonio.ocampo@eez.csic.es.

abiotic stresses. It is known that AM symbiosis can be influenced by other root fungal endophytes, which confer benefits to the host plant, such as growth promotion, protection against disease or enhanced phosphorous uptake. Despite the benefits of these root fungal endophytes for agronomical plants, the physiological and ecological significance of these fungi remains poorly characterized. In this context, we discuss the potential roles of fungal endophytes for growth promotion in *Sorghum*.

In: Food Science Research ... Volume 1
Editor: Lucille Monaco Cacioppo

ISBN: 978-1-63117-932-7
© 2014 Nova Science Publishers, Inc.

Chapter 41

BREEDING FOR ABIOTIC STRESSES IN SORGHUM

Tariq Shehzad and Kazutoshi Okuno[*]

Graduate School of Life and Environmental Sciences,
University of Tsukuba, Tsukuba, Japan

RESEARCH SUMMARY

Mapping and analysis of QTL controlling tolerance to abiotic stresses are primary and significant approaches for germplasm enhancement in crops. In particular, corresponding to global climate changes, improved tolerance to abiotic stresses contributes to crop adaptation and production under stress conditions in crops. The tolerance to abiotic stresses is frequently controlled by multiple genes or quantitative trait loci (QTLs). Identification of QTL using DNA markers is the first strategy in DNA marker-assisted selection (MAS) for the tolerance in sorghum breeding. We assessed salt and drought tolerances using a core collection derived from world germplasm collections of sorghum and detected a broad range of variation. Association analysis was performed using data on genotypes at 98 SSR marker loci and phenotypic values. Major QTL for salt tolerance was mapped on chromosome 1 and closely linked to QTL for leaf senescence. Nine QTL for drought tolerance were also detected. Based on the genetics of tolerance to abiotic stresses, we discussed breeding strategies for abiotic stresses in sorghum.

---

[*] Corresponding author: Prof Kazutoshi Okuno. Email; okuno.kazutoshi.fu@u.tsukuba.ac.jp. Phone: +81-29853-4807; Fax: +81-29853-6617.

In: Food Science Research ... Volume 1
Editor: Lucille Monaco Cacioppo

ISBN: 978-1-63117-932-7
© 2014 Nova Science Publishers, Inc.

Chapter 42

GLUTEN-FREE BREAD: ECONOMIC, NUTRITIONAL AND TECHNOLOGICAL ASPECTS

Maria Teresa Pedrosa Silva Clerici[*1] *and Yoon Kil Chang*[‡2]

[1]Federal University of Alfenas (UNIFAL-MG), Brazil, Alfenas, MG, Brazil
[2] State University of Campinas (UNICAMP), Department of Food Technology – Food
Engineering Faculty, Campinas, SP, Brazil

RESEARCH SUMMARY

This chapter presents a detailed description of previously published works of the economical, nutritional and technological aspects of the research and production of gluten-free bread, which can benefit not only countries that do not produce wheat, but also celiac patients, whose life-long diet completely excludes foods containing wheat, oat, barley, rye and triticale. The real quality of the bread and wheat currently consumed will be investigated in this chapter: the years of research, massive financing by the wheat-exporting countries and private enterprises, high volume of production and intense marketing, all of which contributed to the rise in the global consumption of bread. The quality of gluten-free bread is not yet like that of wheat bread, but this research targets the improvement of the three-dimensional polysaccharide or protein network structure through physical and chemical modifications of starch or protein, so that they may result in wheat-free products of significant technological quality.

*Federal University of Alfenas (UNIFAL-MG), Brazil, Rua Gabriel Monteiro da Silva 700, Centro, CEP 37130-000, Alfenas, MG, Brazil, E-mail: maria.pedrosa@unifal-mg.edu.br, mtcleric@fea.unicamp.br, Telephone: +55-35-3299-1110

‡ State University of Campinas (UNICAMP), Department of Food Technology – Food Engineering Faculty, P.O. Box 6121, Zip Code 13083-862, Campinas, SP, Brazil, E-mail: yokic@fea.unicamp.br, Telephone: +55-19-3521-4001

In: Food Science Research ... Volume 1
Editor: Lucille Monaco Cacioppo

ISBN: 978-1-63117-932-7
© 2014 Nova Science Publishers, Inc.

Chapter 43

IMPACT OF NITROGEN AND SULFUR FERTILIZATION ON GLUTEN COMPOSITION, AND BAKING QUALITY OF WHEAT

*Dorothee Steinfurth, Karl H. Mühling and Christian Zörb**
Christian Albrechts University Kiel,
Institute of Plant Nutrition and Soil Science, Kiel, Germany

RESEARCH SUMMARY

Wheat has a broad genetic potential for the expression of various gluten proteins and is strongly influenced by the environment, e. g. with respect to the fertilization of nitrogen (N) and sulfur (S) during wheat plant development. Nitrogen and S availability markedly change wheat flour and baking quality. However, without adequate management of N and S fertilization, the genetic potential of wheat cannot be exploited. Nitrogen fertilization primarily affects the concentration of gliadines and glutenines as it is source-regulated. Storage protein concentration, particularly of gliadine and glutenine, is highly correlated with loaf volume. The use of three instead of one dressing of fertilizer, especially as a late dressing at ear emergence, the gliadine and glutenine concentration of the grain and, furthermore, loaf volume can be enhanced. However, not only quantity, but also the quality of gluten proteins is important for their composition and characteristics. Despite protein amount being only slightly influenced by increasing S fertilization levels, the composition of gluten proteins is highly affected. Increasing S availability for plants enhances S-containing amino acids, namely cysteine and methionine, which are foremost in S-rich gluten proteins. For an improvement of baking quality, a high concentration of S-rich proteins is of particular importance in order to form an appropriate gluten network within the dough. Additionally, a late S dressing can further improve baking quality, since such a dressing increases the synthesis of high molecular weight (HMW) glutenins that considerably affect baking quality in wheat.

---

* Corresponding author: Christian Zörb czoerb@plantnutrition.uni-kiel.de

S-rich components such as sulfate and glutathione are, moreover, important molecules for the transport and supply of S to the grain. Both these molecules represent important S transport forms from source to sink organs. The potential to synthesize large amounts of storage protein depends on the ability of the plant to take up and to transport S into sink organs such as ears and kernels. Sulfur and glutathione are therefore important molecules functioning as actuators during plant growth and grain development. Furthermore, glutathione can function as internal plant signal for the S status of the plant. In terms of baking quality, glutathione is able to interact with gluten proteins responding in a change of existing disulfide bonds between gluten proteins and resulting in a different rheological property and baking quality. Concerning the interaction of N and S in wheat, a well-balanced N/S ratio is exceedingly important for suitable gluten and baking quality. If high N fertilization is accompanied by inadequate S fertilization, S deficiency is provoked, resulting in changed gluten protein composition and a loss of nutritional quality of the grains.

In: Food Science Research ... Volume 1
Editor: Lucille Monaco Cacioppo

ISBN: 978-1-63117-932-7
© 2014 Nova Science Publishers, Inc.

Chapter 44

FUNCTIONAL GLUTEN ALTERNATIVES

Aleksandra Torbica, Miroslav Hadnađev,
Tamara Dapčević Hadnađev and Petar Dokić
Institute for Food Technology, University of Novi Sad, Novi Sad, Serbia

RESEARCH SUMMARY

The demand for gluten-free products is ascending steadily, paralleling the increase in prevalence and incidence of celiac disease and other allergic reactions or intolerances to gluten consumption. The replacement of gluten presents a major technological challenge, as its visco-elastic properties largely determine the breadmaking performance of wheat flour. Various gluten-free formulations apply mixtures of rice or corn flour and different hydrocolloids or starches to mimic the unique properties of gluten. However, gluten-free products containing gums and starches as gluten replacements lack in essential nutrients. Therefore, replacing standard gluten-free formulations with those made from alternative grains like buckwheat may impart nutritional benefits. This chapter reviews the literature on gluten-free bakery products, including both hydrocolloid-based and pseudo-cereal-based formulations. A special emphasis is given to ongoing research in our laboratory related to gluten-free bread and cookies containing rice and buckwheat flour. The optimal gluten-free formulations were created by comparing the rheological properties of different rice and buckwheat flour mixtures to properties of wheat flour assessed by using Mixolab. Subsequently, rice, buckwheat and wheat flours were evaluated by electrophoretic and electron-microscopic analysis. Moreover, the influence of buckwheat flour type and content on rheological, textural, sensory properties of gluten-free dough, bread and cookies was investigated.

In: Food Science Research ... Volume 1
Editor: Lucille Monaco Cacioppo

ISBN: 978-1-63117-932-7
© 2014 Nova Science Publishers, Inc.

Chapter 45

CHIAROSCURO OF STANDARDIZATION FOR GLUTEN-FREE FOODS LABELING AND GLUTEN QUANTITATION METHODS

A. M. Calderón de la Barca, E. J. Esquer-Munguía and F. Cabrera-Chávez

Centro de Investigación en Alimentación y Desarrollo, A.C.
Hermosillo, Sonora, México

RESEARCH SUMMARY

Celiac disease (CD) is an autoimmune enteropathy characterized by intolerance to wheat gluten. CD patients must adhere to a strict lifelong gluten-free diet, excluding all food products containing wheat and taxonomically related cereals. The CD prevalence is 1% in any population over the world and apparently it is increasing. Thus, the gluten content must be regulated in specialties for gluten intolerant patients by reliable and sensitive methods. To reach this objective, several procedures have been used including immunological and non-immunological methods. Additionally to limitations on gluten quantitation due to the principles of the tests, there are limitations due to the methods of proteins' extraction. In this chapter, troubles and trends for gluten quantitation in gluten-free foodstuffs are discussed. Also differences and agreements on the regulations of gluten-free labeling as well as the related basic definitions are shown. Finally, it is stated the consideration of the industry needs, current scientist knowledge and the safety of gluten intolerant patients for a good regulation and international trade of gluten-free foodstuffs.

In: Food Science Research ... Volume 1
Editor: Lucille Monaco Cacioppo

ISBN: 978-1-63117-932-7
© 2014 Nova Science Publishers, Inc.

Chapter 46

EFFECT OF HEAT ON GLUTEN

Costas E. Stathopoulos and Quan V. Vuong
School of Environmental and Life Sciences,
University of Newcastle, Australia

RESEARCH SUMMARY

The effect of processing, and heat in particular, on the wheat gluten proteins can be difficult to explain due to its complex, and often unusual, rheological and biochemical properties. Heat denaturation of wheat gluten proteins and the accompanying rheological changes, together with a number of interactions, such as hydrogen bonding, SS bonding and hydrophobic interactions have an effect on the native structure of the protein. During the heat treatment of gluten, denaturation, aggregation and cross-linking all combine to give rise to a series of changes that affect rheological and biochemical properties alike. Different components of gluten might exhibit different responses to heat treatment, based on their parent wheat variety, their size, their composition, or the environment the heat treatment took place. Today's food scientists are yet to fully understand all the interactions and mechanisms involved in the effect of heat on gluten but this field of research has grown enormously over the last few decades and continuously expands offering us a better insight and understanding.

In: Food Science Research ... Volume 1
Editor: Lucille Monaco Cacioppo

ISBN: 978-1-63117-932-7
© 2014 Nova Science Publishers, Inc.

Chapter 47

MODERN CONCEPTS PATHOGENESIS OF CELIAC DISEASE: FROM GLUTEN TO AUTOIMMUNITY

Asma Ouakaa-Kchaou[*]

Department of Gastroenterology and Hepatology,
Habib Thameur Hospital, Tunis-Tunisia

RESEARCH SUMMARY

Background: Celiac disease, also known as gluten-sensitive enteropathy and non-tropical sprue, is a prevalent autoimmune disorder that is triggered by the ingestion of gluten and related prolamins in genetically susceptible individuals. The classic celiac lesion occurs in the proximal small intestine with histological changes of intestinal villous atrophy, crypt hyperplasia, intraepithelial lymphocytosis and leukocyte infiltration of the lamina propria. The pathogenic mechanisms in this disease are not yet well understood, but it is clear that genetic, environmental and immunological factors play a role.

Aim: To provide an evidence-based overview of the pathogenesis of celiac disease.

Methods: Review based on relevant medical literature.

Results: Celiac disease is uniquely characterized by a defined trigger (gluten proteins from wheat and related cereals), the necessary presence of HLA-DQ2 or HLA-DQ8, and the generation of circulating autoantibodies. Celiac disease has become one of the best-understood HLA-linked disorders. Well-identified haplotypes in the human leukocyte antigen (HLA) class II region (either DQ2 [DQA*0501-DQB*0201] or DQ8 [DQA*0301-DQB1*0302]) confer a large part of the genetic susceptibility to celiac disease. The immune response in celiac disease involves the adaptive, as well as the innate, and is characterized by the presence of anti-gliadin and anti-transglutaminase antibodies, lymphocytic infiltration in the epithelial membrane and the lamina propria, and expression of multiple cytokines and other signaling proteins.

---

[*] Corresponding author: Ouakaa-Kchaou Asma, Department of Gastroenterology. Habib Thameur Hospital, Address: 8, Ali Ben Ayed Street Montfleury 1008, Tunis - Tunisia., Phone: (00216) 98 383 053, Fax: (00216) 71 493 167, E-mail: asma.kchaou@voilà.fr or asma.kchaou@rns.tn

Conclusion: Gluten-free diet is currently the only effective mode of treatment for celiac disease; nevertheless, there is a growing demand for alternative treatment options. Better understanding of the mechanism of the disease is likely to add other choices for therapy in the future.

In: Food Science Research ... Volume 1
Editor: Lucille Monaco Cacioppo

ISBN: 978-1-63117-932-7
© 2014 Nova Science Publishers, Inc.

Chapter 48

EMULSION PROPERTIES OF DIFFERENT PROTEIN FRACTIONS FROM HYDROLYZED WHEAT GLUTEN

S. R. Drago[1,3], R. J. González[1] and M. C. Añón[2,3]

[1] Instituto de Tecnología de Alimentos -FIQ- Univ. Nacional del Litoral,
Santa Fe, Argentina
[2] CIDCA UNLP-CIC-CONICET, La Plata, Argentina
[3] CONICET CONICET, CIDCA, calle 47 y 116, La Plata, Argentina

RESEARCH SUMMARY

Many protein sources that are found in the market are obtained as by-products and there is a great interest in using them as protein ingredients with adequate functionality for food formulation. Structure modification allows to add value and to diversify their uses. The viscoelastic properties of wheat gluten have restricted its use in baked products, and the diversification of gluten applications depends of the improvement of its solubility in a wider pH range. An alternative for that is the enzymic hydrolysis.

The objective of this work was to evaluate emulsion properties of protein fractions obtained by extracting at 3 pH different hydrolyzed gluten samples.

Hydrolyzates were made using two commercial enzymes (acid and alkaline proteases) to reach 3 different hydrolysis degrees (DH) for each enzyme. Extracts were obtained at 3 different pHs (4, 6.5 and 9) and were diluted to a protein concentration of 4 g/l. Each extract was used to make the corn oil: extract emulsions (25:75, W/W).

Emulsion capacity was determined by measuring droplet size distribution and the stability using a vertical scan macroscopic analyzer.

Regarding emulsion capacity, multifactor ANOVA (factors: pH and DH) made for droplet size distribution parameters showed that there were no differences between samples.

Regarding stability evaluation, alkaline protease extract emulsions were more stable in particle migration phenomena by creaming, but showed higher coalescence rates than those corresponding to acid protease extract emulsions.

It was also observed that for both enzymes, as DH increases, coalescence rates decrease for the 3 pHs extracts and creaming rates increase for pH 4 and 9 extracts. In the case of pH

6.5, acid protease extracts emulsions showed a clear creaming instability by flocculation, probably due to the electrical charges suppression of the peptides adsorbed at the interface, since 6.5 is a pH near the isoelectric point of gluten proteins. It is suggested that acid protease extract emulsions showed a certain degree of bridging flocculation. This caused higher creaming rates but a lower coalescence as a consequence of the bridging. We conclude that although pH of the extraction and DH did not affect emulsion capacity, emulsion stability depended on the pH, DH and the enzyme used.

In: Food Science Research ... Volume 1
Editor: Lucille Monaco Cacioppo

ISBN: 978-1-63117-932-7
© 2014 Nova Science Publishers, Inc.

Chapter 49

TECHNO-FUNCTIONAL PROPERTIES FROM HYDROLYZED WHEAT GLUTEN FRACTIONS

S. R. Drago[1], R. J. González[1] and M. C. Añón[2]

[1] CONICET, Inst. de Tecnología de Alimentos -FIQ- Univ. Nacional del Litoral,
1 de Mayo 3250, Santa Fe, Argentina
[2] CONICET, CIDCA, calle 47 y 116, La Plata, Argentina

RESEARCH SUMMARY

Many protein sources that are found in the market are obtained as by-products and there is a great interest in using them as protein ingredients with adequate functionality for food formulation. Structure modification permits one to add value and to diversify their uses. The diversification of wheat gluten applications depends on the improvement of its solubility in a wider pH range. One of the alternatives that allow protein modification in these products is the enzymic hydrolysis. The objective of this work was to evaluate foaming properties of protein fractions obtained by extracting, at 3 pH, different hydrolyzed gluten samples. Two commercial enzymes (acid -Ac- and alkaline -Al- proteases) were used to reach 3 different hydrolysis degrees (DH). Extracts pHs (4, 6.5 and 9) were diluted to a protein concentration of 4 g/l. RP-HPLC, free amino groups content, sulphydryl and disulfur content, average peptide chain length were used to characterize each extract. Foam was produced by sparging nitrogen at a known rate through a dilute protein solution. The maximal volume of liquid incorporated into the foam (Vmax) and the rate of liquid incorporation into the foam (Ri) were determined and used as indicators of foaming capacity. The times for half-drainage of the liquid that was incorporated into the foam at the end of the bubbling period ($t_{1/2}$) and the rate of liquid drainage from the foam were also measured. Regarding Ri, all pH 4 extracts from hydrolyzed samples showed higher Ri than an un-hydrolyzed sample. Extracts from Al hydrolyzed extracts showed higher Ri than those from Ac. In the case of Al extracts, an inverse relation between DH and Ri was observed, but practically no influence of DH on Ri, was observed in the case of Ac extracts. For pH 6.5 extracts, the relation between DH and Ri were in opposite directions, depending on the enzyme, for Ac, Ri decreased with DH, while for Al, Ri increased with DH. At this pH, it was observed that the extracts which foamed more quickly, were those with the highest times for half-drainage of the liquid ($t_{1/2}$). Some foam parameters correlated between themselves, depending on the extracts. Foaming capacity and stability depend on pH, DH and enzyme and it was possible to correlate parameters with composition evaluated by RP-HPLC.

In: Food Science Research … Volume 1
Editor: Lucille Monaco Cacioppo

ISBN: 978-1-63117-932-7
© 2014 Nova Science Publishers, Inc.

Chapter 50

GLUTEN-FREE DIET IN CHILDREN AND ADOLESCENTS WITH CELIAC DISEASE

Gian Vincenzo Zuccotti, Dario Dilillo, Fabio Meneghin and Cecilia Mantegazza
University of Milan, Luigi Sacco Hospital, Italy

RESEARCH SUMMARY

Celiac disease (CD) is defined as a permanent sensitivity to the gluten in wheat and related proteins found in barley and rye, which occurs in genetically susceptible individuals and affects 0.5-1% of the general population worldwide. Currently, the only available treatment is lifelong adherence to a gluten-free diet (GFD). There is evidence that untreated CD is associated with a significant increase in morbidity and mortality. It has been demonstrated that even small amounts of ingested gluten can lead to mucosal changes upon intestinal biopsy. Previously, products containing less than 200 ppm (<200 mg/kg) were regarded as gluten-free. Currently, less than 20 ppm (<20 mg/kg) is being considered in the proposed Codex Alimentarius Guidelines to define gluten-free. In the USA, the national food authority has recently redefined their definition of "gluten-free" with a threshold of no gluten. The use of oats is not widely recommended because of concerns about potential contamination during the harvesting and milling process, so unless the purity of oats can be guaranteed, its safety remains questionable.

A GFD has both lifestyle and financial implications for patients; thus, it can adversely impact their quality of life, such as difficulties eating out, a negative impact on career and family life, anxieties about social difficulties, and feeling different. Though the compliance to a GFD started in childhood is very high, the percentage of adolescents with CD who strictly follow a GFD varies from 43% to 81%; a greater adherence is found within patients with typical symptoms. Moreover, the alimentary habits of healthy adolescents exhibit nutritional imbalances with a high consumption of lipids and proteins and a low consumption of carbohydrates, calcium, fiber and iron; several studies show that adherence to a strict GFD worsens the nutritional imbalances of an adolescent with CD.

Gluten-free products are often low in B and D vitamins, calcium, iron, zinc, magnesium, folate, thiamine, riboflavin, and niacin. Very few commercially available gluten-free products are enriched. Vitamin and mineral supplementation can be useful adjunct therapy for a GFD. Patients inadequately treated have low bone mineral density, imbalanced macronutrients, low fiber intake, and micronutrient deficiencies.

Moreover, recent research has found that adults on a strict GFD for years have high total plasma homocysteine levels; this finding is associated with a high prevalence of being overweight and represents an increased risk for metabolic and cardiovascular disease.

In: Food Science Research ... Volume 1
Editor: Lucille Monaco Cacioppo

ISBN: 978-1-63117-932-7
© 2014 Nova Science Publishers, Inc.

Chapter 51

TECHNOLOGICAL AND HEALTH ASPECTS OF PROBIOTIC CHEESE

Barbaros Özer[1] and Hüseyin Avni Kırmacı[2]*

[1] Abant Izzet Baysal University Faculty of Engineering and Architecture,
Department of Food Engineering, Bolu, Turkey
[2] Harran University Faculty of Agriculture Department of Food Engineering,
Sanliurfa, Turkey

RESEARCH SUMMARY

There have been numerous scientific studies on the incorporation of probiotic bacteria into foods in the literature since their health promoting effects have been well established about two decades ago. Among the foods, dairy products have a distinct place in delivering probiotics into human gut, as these products provide probiotic bacteria with a suitable environment in which their growth are stimulated. During the last two decades, significant attention has been paid to fermented dairy products containing probiotic bacteria originating from the human intestine. Up until now, physical, chemical and sensory properties of such products have been well documented and some products have already been commercialized. However, probiotics may show rather low viability in yogurt and other fermented dairy products due to their acidic nature. Because of its higher pH, fat content and more solid consistency, cheese offers certain advantages over fermented milk products in terms of delivering viable probiotics to the human gut and, therefore, has been considered to be an ideal vehicle for probiotic uptake. Although, cheese provides many advantages regarding probiotic uptake, the growth and viability of probiotics in cheese depend largely on manufacturing practices. Cheddar type scalded cheeses, for example, have been proved to be more suitable for inclusion of probiotics than brined or high cooked cheeses. Stimulative or inhibitive effect(s) of metabolites generated by classical cheese starters and/or natural cheese flora on the probiotics is another issue that needs to be investigated in detail. The relationship between probiotic adjuncts and the quality of the cheeses after ripening or maturation is yet to

---

* Corresponding author: adabarbaros@gmail.com.

be established for many varieties. Finally, in the most recent works, some probiotic strains have been shown to be able to produce bioactive peptides and angiotensin converting enzyme-inhibitor peptides (ACE-I) which further contributes to their already established health promoting effects. This review details technological advances shown to be effective in the incorporation of probiotic bacteria into cheeses and techniques for the accurate enumeration of these bacteria in the presence of complex cheese flora. The systematic approach for the screening probiotic effect in fresh and mature cheeses, impact of the processing parameters on viability of probiotics, methods of protecting probiotics against harsh environmental conditions in cheese (i.e. microencapsulation, addition of probiotics, effective packaging etc.) and health aspects of probiotics with specific reference to cheese applications are also included in this review.

In: Food Science Research ... Volume 1
Editor: Lucille Monaco Cacioppo

ISBN: 978-1-63117-932-7
© 2014 Nova Science Publishers, Inc.

Chapter 52

THE RELATIONSHIP BETWEEN GENETIC AND TECHNOLOGICAL ASPECTS AND CHEESE QUALITY

M. Fresno* and S. Álvarez

Unidad de Producción Animal Pastos y Forrajes. Instituto Canario de Investigaciones Agrarias. Apdo. La Laguna, S/C de Tenerife, Spain

RESEARCH SUMMARY

Cheese quality is dependent on its physiochemical composition and sensory properties. These factors are influenced by milk composition, which, in turn, depends on the structure of the feed ingested by the dairy animals. However, technological and genetic aspects can also interact and can often mask the effect of diet in addition to being an important source of quality variation. Studies investigating the role of genetic factors (species and breed) in cheese quality frequently take place looking at differences between cheeses made with a local breed's milk and those elaborated with milk from international breeds. In addition, the autochthonous genotypes are usually linked to labelled products and normally have higher concentration of certain milk components, such as protein and casein. The relationship between genotype and quality is mainly linked to changes in milk quality that modify the physicochemical composition of cheeses that affect the nutritional value of the product. Furthermore, technological parameters also influence changes of cheese quality. The two traditional cheese-making practices, type of rennet and smoking process, can play an important role in cheese quality in two different ways: to recover traditional characteristics of Protected Denomination of Origin cheeses or other labelled products, and to impart different organoleptic properties to new products. These cheese-making practices can be useful commercial tools for cheese producers to identify and differentiate their products in current global market. The type of rennet used has an important influence in milk clotting and cheese quality. Artisan rennet (kids or lambs) pastes and traditional vegetable coagulants, especially

---

* Email: mfresno@icia.es.

different species of the *Cynara* genus, affect fat, protein fraction and sensory profile. Smoking, together with drying and salting, is one of the oldest food preservation techniques. Smoke has an antioxidant and bacteriostatic action; it also dries the rind of the cheeses and contributes to their conservation. In modern food technology, smoking is no longer considered as food preservation practice and the primary purpose of this technique is to give the product a characteristic taste, texture and appearance. Where smoked products are concerned, the most important feature of consumer choice is distinctiveness in the sensory properties. The purpose of the present chapter is to analyze how genetic aspects and some technological practices (type of rennet and smoking process) affect cheese quality.

In: Food Science Research ... Volume 1
Editor: Lucille Monaco Cacioppo

ISBN: 978-1-63117-932-7
© 2014 Nova Science Publishers, Inc.

Chapter 53

AUTHENTICATION OF LOCAL CHEESES: A GLOBAL PERSPECTIVE

Ahmet Koluman, Rind Kürşat Aktaş and Abdullah Dikici

National Food Reference Laboratory, Ankara, Republic of Turkey

RESEARCH SUMMARY

Globalization of food sources triggered a demand and public tendency for organic foods and local products. This demand caused a massive application for patenting the local products. With this perspective, authentication studies for all food products have been started globally. Like all food other types cheese has become one of the major subject for authentication process. Authentication includes patenting and under the defined names are: Protected Designation of Origin (PDO) and Protected Geographical Origin (PGO). "Geographical indications (GI)" is also a term for proving the authentication with geographical parameters. European Union (EU) has started to use the patenting approach at their local products on 12 June 1996 with "Commission Regulation (EC) No 1107/96" of the registration of geographical indications and designations of origin under the procedure laid down in "Article 17 of Council Regulation (EEC) No 2081/92". This regulation leads to PDO and PGO patenting of different food products including cheese. Some samples for patenting of authentic cheeses can be listed as; Beacon Fell traditional Lancashire cheese (PDO), Bonchester cheese (PDO), Buxton blue (PDO), Dorset Blue cheese (GI), Dovedale cheese (PDO), Exmoor Blue cheese (PGO), Single Gloucester (PDO), Staffordshire Cheese (PDO), Swaledale cheese (PDO), Swaledale ewes' cheese (PDO), Teviotdale cheese (GI), Stilton - White cheese (PDO), Stilton - Blue cheese (PDO), West Country farmhouse Cheddar cheese (see Cheddar cheese) (PDO).

This chapter aims to summarize definitions of authentic and local products, PDO, PGO, and GI. On the other hand, it underlines the regulations for authentication, makes a comprehensive review for PDO, PGO and GI procedures and sustainability for authentic cheese production. Global supply and demand for authentic cheeses and labeling of these cheeses is also given under this chapter.

In: Food Science Research ... Volume 1
Editor: Lucille Monaco Cacioppo

ISBN: 978-1-63117-932-7
© 2014 Nova Science Publishers, Inc.

Chapter 54

SPANISH BLUE CHEESES: FUNCTIONAL METABOLITES

Sivia M. Albillos[1], Carlos García-Estrada[1] and Juan-Francisco Martín[1,2]

[1] Instituto de Biotecnología de León (INBIOTEC),
Parque Científico de León, León, Spain
[2] Área de Microbiología, Departamento de Biología Molecular, Universidad de León,
Campus de Vegazana s/n; León, Spain

RESEARCH SUMMARY

Blue cheeses are produced from cow's milk, sheep's milk, or goat's milk depending on the variety. They always have *Penicillium* cultures added, along with the lactic acid bacteria starter cultures (*Lactococcus lactis* and *Leuconostoc cremoris*), so that the final product is spotted or veined throughout with blue, blue-gray or blue-green mold. The aftertaste is a little salty and sharp and its characteristic smell is often produced by metabolites released by the bacteria *Brevibacterium linens*. *Penicillium roqueforti* utilizes β-ketoacyl-CoA deacylase (thiohydrolase) and β-ketoacid decarboxylase to provide the compounds typical for the aroma of the blue semi-soft cheeses. The production of blue cheeses is basically concentrated on a few countries around the world, such as France, Spain, Italy, England and Denmark. Throughout history, there are vestiges that the Roquefort region produced cheese as long as 3,500 years ago, being often considered a delicatessen and prohibitive because of its costly price and political reasons. Roquefort has been named as the "king of cheeses" or the "cheese of the king" due to the veneration that the emperor Charlemagne and several French kings had for this type of product.

In Spain, several blue-veined cheeses of excellent quality are produced, being the region on the north area of Picos de Europa the one with more varieties (Cabrales, Valdeón, Bejes-Tresviso, Picón, among others that carry a legally Protected Designation of Origin). Our research group has recently studied some of these varieties and characterized the *Penicillium* species present in the blue cheese. Interestingly, we have found that *P. roqueforti*, the main of these species, produces important secondary metabolites with functional properties, such as the antitumor andrastins and mycophenolic acid, together with mycotoxins (roquefortine C and PR toxin). Efforts have been made by our group in order to shed light on the biosynthetic pathways for those secondary metabolites with the aim of engineering *P. roqueforti* strains with an added value for the cheese industry.

In: Food Science Research ... Volume 1   ISBN: 978-1-63117-932-7
Editor: Lucille Monaco Cacioppo   © 2014 Nova Science Publishers, Inc.

Chapter 55

SODIUM IN DIFFERENT CHEESE TYPES: ROLE AND STRATEGIES OF REDUCTION

Mamdouh El-Bakry[1,2]

[1]UCD School of Agriculture, Food Science and Veterinary Medicine, Dublin, Ireland
[2]Department of Dairy Science and Technology, Faculty of Agriculture, Cairo University, Giza, Egypt

RESEARCH SUMMARY

Cheese is a versatile, nutrient-dense dairy food, i.e. a good source of protein, vitamins and minerals particularly calcium and phosphorus, which is an important component in highly consumed convenience foods (O'Brien and O'Connor, 2004). However, cheese is perceived as being high in saturated fat, which might contribute to risks of atherosclerosis, and sodium (Johnson et al., 2009). There is considerable evidence that high sodium intake, which is the case in Western countries, is associated with hypertension and strokes, hence, dietary guidelines recommend that sodium intake be reduced.

This chapter covers the scientific and technological aspects of the role of sodium in cheese manufacture and functional properties and highlights various strategies for reducing the sodium. The focus is on natural cheese, made from milk by acid and/or rennet-coagulation, and process cheese. This cheese differs from natural cheese in that it is made from natural cheese or casein, which is blended with the necessary emulsifying salts and in the presence of heat, leading to the formation of a homogeneous product with extended shelf-life (Zehren and Nusbaum, 2000). Process cheese has numerous end-use applications in processed foods, which counts for ~75% of the dietary sodium in industrialized diets (Doyle and Glass, 2010).

The source of sodium in cheese is mainly the added salt (sodium chloride). Salt acts primarily as food preservative and flavor enhancer and also interacts with major components in the cheese and thereby affecting the functionality, e.g. salt increases the protein hydration during manufacture which affects the stability and textural properties (Johnson et al., 2009). Process cheese contains much higher sodium content, compared to natural cheese, due to the necessity of using emulsifying salts, such as sodium citrate and phosphate. These salts are crucial for the hydration of the protein, emulsification of fat and the stability of the final product.

Strategies for reducing sodium in cheese are mainly outlined in the reduction of the salt and/or emulsifying salts used and their substitution by the potassium equivalents salts. However, these strategies present many challenges, such as adverse effects on flavor and microbiological stability. In process cheese, a high reduction of emulsifying salts does not allow for the formation of a homogeneous end product. Recent approaches of reducing emulsifying salts used are also discussed, such as utilizing of emulsifiers or protein hydrolyzates in the manufacture of cheese (Zehren and Nusbaum, 2000).

A final section in this chapter is about the future of low sodium cheese manufacture, including suggestions for reducing sodium which has not been systematically investigated in research on various cheese types.

In: Food Science Research ... Volume 1
Editor: Lucille Monaco Cacioppo

ISBN: 978-1-63117-932-7
© 2014 Nova Science Publishers, Inc.

Chapter 56

INVESTIGATION ON A TYPICAL DAIRY PRODUCT OF THE APULIA REGION (ITALY), THE GARGANICO CACIORICOTTA CHEESE, BY MEANS OF TRADITIONAL AND INNOVATIVE PHYSICO-CHEMICAL ANALYSES

A. Sacco,* D. Sacco, G. Casiello, A. Ventrella and F. Longobardi

Dipartimento di Chimica, Università di Bari "A. Moro", Via Orabona 4,
Bari (Italy)

RESEARCH SUMMARY

This work deals with the characterization of a typical goat cheese, cacioricotta, produced in a restricted area (Promontory of Gargano) of the Apulia Region in Southern Italy. For this purpose, conventional (fat, protein, casein, urea, cryoscopy, metals content, fatty acid composition, solid content, moisture, ashes, pH) and innovative physico-chemical analyses, such as Nuclear Magnetic Resonance (NMR) Spectroscopy and Isotope Ratio Mass Spectroscopy (IRMS), have been carried out. The determinations have been done both on the starting goat milk and on the obtained cheese after 20 and 60 days of ripening. The conventional analysis has allowed to follow compositional changes of some elements occurred during the ripening of cacioricotta cheese. The NMR spectra were recorded using two different procedures. In the former, the sample was prepared by means of an aqueous extraction of the cacioricotta, while in the latter, the analysis was performed directly on the cacioricotta sample by using the ^{1}H HR-MAS NMR technique. All spectroscopic results have allowed the identification of the metabolic profile of cacioricotta cheese. Finally, for the first time, the IRMS has been applied on goat milk and cheese. The obtained isotopic results were

* Correspondent author: Prof. Antonio Sacco, Dipartimento di Chimica, Via Orabona 4, 70126 Bari (Italy). e-mail: antonio.sacco@chimica.uniba.it.

not easy to understand and required further investigations on a higher number of samples. Moreover, a comparison of results of cacioricotta samples coming from different areas of production could be very interesting.

In: Food Science Research ... Volume 1
Editor: Lucille Monaco Cacioppo

ISBN: 978-1-63117-932-7
© 2014 Nova Science Publishers, Inc.

Chapter 57

Slovak Bryndza Cheese

Roman Dušinský, Libor Ebringer, Mária Mikulášová, Anna Belicová and Juraj* Krajčovič

Institute of Cell Biology and Biotechnology, Faculty of Natural Sciences,
Comenius University, Mlynská dolina, Bratislava, Slovakia

Research Summary

Slovak Bryndza cheese is a traditional type of cheese closely associated with the history and culture of Slovakia. "Slovenská bryndza" (Slovak Bryndza cheese) has been granted European Protected Geographical Indication (PGI) status. The matured sheep lump cheese alone or mixed with cow cheese is crushed and ground to give rise to soft, spreadable, salty Bryndza cheese. At present, commercially available Bryndza cheese can legally contain up to 49% cow cheese and the traditional technology is influenced by sophisticated milking machines and by thermal processing of the ewes' milk. Characteristic aroma and taste of the traditional Bryndza cheese are the result of the presence of a high amount of natural microorganisms, especially lactic acid bacteria (*Lactobacillus, Enterococcus, Lactococcus*) and partly micromycetes (*Kluyveromyces, Galactomyces, Mucor*) as well. Food safety of the unpasteurized product is ensured by a technological process of fermentation. Keeping sheep on the mountainous meadows makes Bryndza cheese really healthy because of the rich content of unsaturated fatty acids (ALA – alpha linolenic acid, CLA – conjugated linoleic acid), an appropriate amount of minerals and a relatively high content of vitamins and natural positive microflora. Beneficial attributes of the traditional Bryndza cheese in human health and nutrition are being researched. Bryndza cheese is mostly eaten as a topping on small boiled potato dumplings (with pieces of fried bacon) as a Slovak national meal called "Bryndzové halušky" (Bryndza cheese dumplings). It is also often used as a spread on a piece of bread or as a compound of more complex spreads, filling for pasta and pies, or used in a soup. Sheep farming and Bryndza cheese is a part of the unique and specific Slovak folk culture tradition which influenced and boosted tourism, including various annual festivals,

---

* Corresponding author: E-mail: krajcovic@fns.uniba.sk.

e.g. the World Championship of Cooking and Eating Bryndza Cheese Dumplings or "Ovenalie" – Shepherd's Sunday.

In: Food Science Research … Volume 1
Editor: Lucille Monaco Cacioppo

ISBN: 978-1-63117-932-7
© 2014 Nova Science Publishers, Inc.

Chapter 58

PROCESSED CHEESE: RELEVANCE FOR LOW SODIUM CHEESE DEVELOPMENT

Adriano G. Cruz[1], Adriane E.C. Antunes[2], Renata M.S. Celeguini[1], Jose A.F. Faria[1] and Marise Aparecida Rodrigues Pollonio[1]

[1] FEA/UNICAMP- Faculdade de Engenharia de Alimentos (Faculty of Food Engineering)/ Universidade de Campinas (UNICAMP)
[2] FCA/UNICAMP – Faculdade de Ciências Aplicadas (School of Applied Sciences) / Universidade Estadual de Campinas (University of Campinas)

RESEARCH SUMMARY

Sodium is a mineral widely consumed in human diets, bestowing pleasant sensory characteristics when added to foods at certain concentrations.

Besides, salt was a precious commodity and was also an emblem of immortality and a symbol of immutable loyalty. This is reflected for instance by the act of sharing bread and salt with a guest—still practised in Slavic countries (Ritz, 2006). Sodium consumption is even quoted in the Holy Bible in three of the four Gospels (Matthew 5: 13-14, Mark 9, 50 and Luke 14, 34): "You are the salt of the earth. But if the salt loses its saltiness, how it be made salty again?". Certainly, the motivation of biblical quotations were using elements of daily life to explain the religious values and not properly discuss salt consumption in the population.

It has been recommended by government-appointed bodies and nutrition experts a reduction in salt intake from the current average consumption of 10–12 g to an expected intake of 5–6 g/day (Abbott et al., 1994). The amount of sodium chloride in the diet of industrialized nations far exceeds physical requirements. The deliberate addition of salt to food only began 5,000 – 10,000 years ago at the beginning of agriculture and farming so that the present consumption of 10 g/day on average is, in evolutionary terms, relatively recent (Meneton et al., 2005).

Greater consumption of sodium is due to the increase of salt to food and increasing consumption of processed foods, which tend to have high amounts of the mineral due to its sensory properties and property salt that act as a helper for food conservation. We stress that the human diet without sodium chloride already present naturally a percentage of this mineral, because many food items have intrinsic sodium. In the past, food consumed by terrestrial mammals, including primates, never contained a lot of salt. Indeed, except for rare cases, plants contain only traces of salt, and the consumption of very large amounts of fruits, roots, leaves, or seeds does not bring much salt in the organism (Meneton et al., 2005). For omnivorous and carnivorous species, the occasional or regular absorption of meat increases salt intake, but in limited proportions because the eaten meat corresponds most often to the sodium-poor intracellular medium and not to the sodium-rich extracellular medium that is generally lost when the animal is killed or cooked (Meneton et al., 2005).

Under healthy conditions almost 90% of sodium ingested is excreted through urine, thus, the urinary sodium represents a reliable biochemical marker of dietary intake of this mineral (Dawson-Hughes, 2009). Although the human body in health status is able to efficiently eliminate sodium from dietary source, the high consumption of that macromineral may have two important adverse effects: (1) raising systemic blood pressure and (2) causing an increase in renal calcium excretion, which may contribute to long-term osteoporosis.

In: Food Science Research ... Volume 1
Editor: Lucille Monaco Cacioppo

ISBN: 978-1-63117-932-7
© 2014 Nova Science Publishers, Inc.

Chapter 59

ITALIAN CHEESE TYPES AND INNOVATIONS OF TRADITIONAL CHEESES

Palmiro Poltronieri, Maria Stella Cappello, Federico Baruzzi, and Maria Morea

National Research Council of Italy, CNR-ISPA,
Institute of Sciences of Food Productions, Lecce, Italy

RESEARCH SUMMARY

Dairy productions in the Italian area are rich in fresh soft cheeses, spreadable cheese, like Crescenza and Gorgonzola, fresh type cheeses, like Primo sale and Cacioricotta, and ripened cream types, such as Ricotta forte.

Manufacturing trends and consumer novel products influenced the development of different innovative dairy products such as cheeses containing probiotic microorganisms. These cheese productions help the sustainable development and growth of local producers increasing the economy of dairy factories through the development of products dedicated to individuals with special dietary requirements.

In: Food Science Research ... Volume 1
Editor: Lucille Monaco Cacioppo

ISBN: 978-1-63117-932-7
© 2014 Nova Science Publishers, Inc.

Chapter 60

NMR SPECTROSCOPY IN DAIRY PRODUCTS CHARACTERIZATION

Elvino Brosio and *Raffaella Gianferri*

Department of Chemistry (*V. Cagliolti Building*),
University of Rome *La Sapienza*

RESEARCH SUMMARY

A low- and high-resolution nuclear magnetic resonance spectroscopy based protocol to characterise traditional Italian cheese as *Mozzarella di Bufala Campana* and *Grana Padano* is reported. Low-resolution relaxometry was used for studying the state and distribution of water in different structural elements of cheese resulting from the production process. High-resolution NMR allowed definition of the "chemical fingerprint", the cheese complex matrix profile of low molecular weight metabolites extracted from *Mozzarella* and *Grana Padano*. Both low-resolution and high-resolution NMR seem to provide useful parameters that could be used for monitoring structure and evolution of PDO Italian cheese.

* P.le Aldo Moro, 5 – 00185 Roma, Italy. Telephone: #39 06 49913307, fax: #39 06 490324, e-mail: elvino.brosio@uniroma1.it.

In: Food Science Research ... Volume 1
Editor: Lucille Monaco Cacioppo

ISBN: 978-1-63117-932-7
© 2014 Nova Science Publishers, Inc.

Chapter 61

CHEESE FLAVORS: CHEMICAL ORIGINS AND DETECTION

Michael H. Tunick
Dairy and Functional Foods Research Unit,
Eastern Regional Research Center,
Agricultural Research Service,
U.S. Department of Agriculture,
Wyndmoor, PA, US

RESEARCH SUMMARY

The hundreds of flavor compounds found in cheese arise from the proteins, lipids, and carbohydrates it contains. Flavor compounds are products of diverse reactions that occur in milk during processing, in curd during manufacture, and in cheese during storage, and are detected by a number of methods. Acids, alcohols, aldehydes, esters, ketones, and lactones may all form in cheese depending on the variety. The different pathways of flavor compound formation result from the feed or grass consumed by the animals, enzymes present in the starter culture microorganisms, any adjunct cultures or molds that have been added, the action of the coagulant, and the time and temperature of aging. An assortment of techniques for extracting and identifying flavors has been developed over the years. Gas chromatography and sensory analysis are used to examine these compounds. This chapter will cover the origins of cheese flavors and the ways that scientists can examine them.

In: Food Science Research … Volume 1
Editor: Lucille Monaco Cacioppo

ISBN: 978-1-63117-932-7
© 2014 Nova Science Publishers, Inc.

Chapter 62

ANTIHYPERTENSIVE PEPTIDES FOUND IN CHEESE

F. Javier Espejo, M. Carmen Almécija, Antonio Guadix, and Emilia M. Guadix

Department of Chemical Engineering, University of Granada, Spain

RESEARCH SUMMARY

The production and ripening of cheese involves some biochemical transformations such as the proteolysis of caseins by enzymes associated to lactic acid bacteria. It has been found that these hydrolytic processes may promote the release of a significant amount of peptides with biological activity.

Among the bioactivities described in the scientific literature, peptides which inhibit the angiotensin converting enzyme (ACE) are highlighted because their potential health benefit for hypertension. ACE is a zinc metallopeptidase which converts a biologically inactive polypeptide, angiotensin I, to a potent vasoconstrictor, angiotensin II. Furthermore, ACE catalyses the degradation of bradykinin, a blood pressure lowering nonapeptide. By these actions, ACE raises blood pressure, and therefore, inhibition of this enzyme results in an antihypertensive effect.

In this chapter, it will be reviewed the presence and bioavailability of ACE-inhibitory peptides in a wide array of cheeses from different world regions, including some well-known types such as Cheddar, Mozzarella, Camembert or Manchego. The analytical techniques for quantification and purification of these peptides will be presented. Moreover, procedures for the determination of the antihypertensive effect will be explained for both in vitro and in vivo methods.

In: Food Science Research … Volume 1
Editor: Lucille Monaco Cacioppo

ISBN: 978-1-63117-932-7
© 2014 Nova Science Publishers, Inc.

Chapter 63

NEW APPROACHMENT ON CHOLESTEROL REMOVAL IN CHEESE

Hae-Soo Kwak

Department of Food Science and Technology,
Sejong University, Seoul, Korea

RESEARCH SUMMARY

Cheese is a nutritious food with various balanced nutrients, such as proteins, peptides, amino acids, fats, fatty acids, vitamins and minerals. However, the amounts of cholesterol is very high, e.g. 102mg/100g Cheddar cheese. Most of consumers are not prefer the cholesterol. Dairy scientists have been tried for lowering the cholesterol in cheeses for a long time. The method found initially is reducing fat in cheese that is poor in taste. Recently, we have been studied about removing specifically cholesterol during cheese making without changing anything from cheese including nutrients, flavor, taste and texture. The method developed is entrapping cholesterol by crosslinked β-cyclodextrin (β-CD). Cholesterol can be removed from milk for soft cheeses and from cream for semi hard and hard cheeses. In cholesterol-removed Cheddar cheese ripening, ripening time could be shortened about 50%. Crosslinked β-CD is lower solubility than β-CD, and particle size is bigger. So entrapment and separation from cream are possible and the β-CD is recyclable about 10times. We developed various cholesterol-removed cheeses, such as Cheddar cheese, Mozzarella cheese, Camembert cheese, blue cheese, Gouda cheese, Feta cheese and process cheese. Cholesterol-removed cheeses will be commercialized in near future. I will describe the developed technique in detail in this chapter.

In: Food Science Research ... Volume 1
Editor: Lucille Monaco Cacioppo

ISBN: 978-1-63117-932-7
© 2014 Nova Science Publishers, Inc.

Chapter 64

CHEESE TYPES

Jee-Young Imm[1] and In-Hyu Bae[2]

[1]Department of Foods and Nutrition, Kookmin University, Seoul, Korea
[2]Department of Animal Science, Sunchon National University, Sunchon, Korea

RESEARCH SUMMARY

Classification of more than 500 cheeses is very difficult task. Although classification of cheeses based on single criterion is not perfect or satisfactory grouping of cheese would be necessary to understand similarities and differences of a variety of cheeses. Cheese can be commonly classified by texture (water content) or rind and further classified by ripening microorganism such as bacteria, mold or combination. The most common classifications for cheese are fresh, soft, semi-soft, firm and hard. Within the same classification they have similarities in taste and textures. Fresh cheese includes world famous mozzarella, cottage, those are particularly used for Pizza and Italian dishes. Brie and Camembert belongs to pungent soft cheese. Semi-hard cheeses are recognized by texture of "not too hard" and" not too firm." Blue cheese such as Roquefort, Gorgonzola is characterized by distinctive blue greens color and strong flavor. Emmental and Gruyeres cheeses are representative firm Swiss cheese and contain medium size holes formed by propionic fermentation. World reknown Cheddar cheese also belongs to this class. Hard cheese such as Grana Padano and Pecorino Romano cheeses have the lowest water content and typical grainy texture. They have long aging time and produced for grating purpose.

In: Food Science Research ... Volume 1
Editor: Lucille Monaco Cacioppo

ISBN: 978-1-63117-932-7
© 2014 Nova Science Publishers, Inc.

Chapter 65

WORLD PRODUCTION AND CONSUMPTION OF CHEESE

Suk-Ho Choi[1] and Se-Jong Oh[2]

[1]Department of Animal Science and Biotechnology, Sangji University, Wonju, Korea
[2]Department of Animal Science, Chonnam National University, Gwangju, Korea

RESEARCH SUMMARY

World production of industrial cheeses has reached 17.0 million tons in 2009. The countries in Europe and northern America produced and consumed about 80% of cheeses in the world. Cheese production and consumption worldwide steadily increased during the period from 2000 to 2007 due both to demand for commodity cheeses, such as Mozzarella, Cheddar, and other cheeses of prospering fast food outlets and restaurants and to rising incomes in both non-EU European countries, such as Russia, Belarus and Ukraine, and developing countries, such as Brazil, Republic Korea. Cheese production and consumption of New Zealand and Australia stagnated and decreased, which can be attributed to both to stagnating milk supplies and to decreasing cheese export. The cheese production and consumption were negatively affected by the financial crisis and following economic depression in 2008. The cheese trade outpaced cheese production during the period from 2000 to 2009. EU, New Zealand and Australia are leading cheese exporters, while Russia and Japan are noticeable cheese importers. Cheese importing countries are located rather widely throughout the world.

In: Food Science Research ... Volume 1
Editor: Lucille Monaco Cacioppo

ISBN: 978-1-63117-932-7
© 2014 Nova Science Publishers, Inc.

Chapter 66

SHIITAKE MUSHROOM SUBMERGED CULTURE AND MORPHOGENESIS: REGULARITIES, COMPUTATIONS, PRACTICAL USE

Olga M. Tsivileva[1]*, Alexei N. Pankratov[2]+
and Valentina E. Nikitina[1]

[1]Laboratory of Microbiology, Institute of Biochemistry and Physiology
of Plants and Microorganisms, Russian Academy of Sciences,
Saratov, Russia
[2]Division of Analytical Chemistry and Chemical Ecology,
Institute of Chemistry, N. G. Chernyshevskii Saratov State University,
Saratov, Russia

RESEARCH SUMMARY

The advantage of submerged mushroom culture for the production of mushroom derivatives is clear: mycelia formed by growing pure strains in submerged culture under controlled conditions not only have a consistent composition, but are also safer. One of the first macrofungi to be cultivated at large scale in submerged culture was the basidiomycete *Lentinula edodes* (Berk.) Pegler, otherwise known as shiitake.

The topics on submerged cultivation related to biosynthesis of extracellular polysaccharides and other medicinal substances are covered. Attention is paid to the extracellular proteins production (oxidative enzymes, ribonucleases, enzymatic activity in dual cultures of *Lentinula*) and morphogenesis in liquid culture.

Then we turn our attention to the results that our group has obtained working with *L. edodes* over the last ten years.

* Corresponding author: Olga M. Tsivileva. E-mail: tsivileva@ibppm.sgu.ru
+ E-mail: PankratovAN@info.sgu.ru

The formation of pigmented mycelial film in submerged culture was assayed to find correlations with both the medium composition and the age of inoculums. The quantum chemical methods and QSAR were applied to test our supposition that a differential character of interaction between the amino acids under study and Ca^{2+}, Mn^{2+} cations should be related not to the distinct electron structures of zwitter ions, but most likely to their differing hydrophobicity.

The growth parameters and the dynamics of lectin activity of *L. edodes* on liquid media enriched with selenium in the organic form have been studied. Diacetophenonylselenide (DAPS-25) exerts the appreciably positive effect upon the vital processes of *L. edodes*.

The effort to explain the metal cations effect on the lectin activity of *L. edodes* from the viewpoint of quantum chemical considerations has been attempted, starting from the dynamics of change in the extracellular lectins activity in the presence of double-charged cations of iron, cobalt, nickel in the composition of liquid synthetic culture medium.

The dependence of periods before fruiting of *L. edodes* upon the presence of divalent manganese in the liquid media, when growing the seeding mycelium by submerged cultivation, has been explored. Provided that Mn^{2+} enters the composition of liquid medium, so the considerable decrease in the duration of periods before both the brown mycelial film formation in liquid culture and the fruit bodies appearance on using the intermediate seeding culture thus obtained, has been observed.

The feasibility has been examined and the parameters selected for the co-cultivation of *L. edodes* and bacteria from *Azospirillum* genus. The co-culture of *Lentunus* sp. and *Azospirillum* sp. has been never studied previously. An explicit advantage of co-culture with respect to its capability of suppressing the microfloral contamination has been noted.

The characterization of the group of extracellular indolic compounds of *L. edodes* in relation to the submerged cultivation conditions has been presented.

Based on the aforesaid, several novel methods for growing the seeding mycelium of shiitake have been proposed and confirmed by national patents.

In: Food Science Research … Volume 1
Editor: Lucille Monaco Cacioppo

ISBN: 978-1-63117-932-7
© 2014 Nova Science Publishers, Inc.

Chapter 67

EDIBLE MUSHROOMS: POTENTIAL ROLE IN WEIGHT REGULATION

Kavita H. Poddar, Mary Jo Feeney and Lawrence J. Cheskin
Johns Hopkins Bloomberg School of Public Health,
Baltimore, Maryland, US

RESEARCH SUMMARY

Mushrooms are a class of "macrofungi" which in recent years have gained popularity among general consumers and the scientific community. Edible mushrooms have been shown to possess high nutritive value, and are being considered as "nutraceuticals" due to their potential health benefits. *In vitro* and *in vivo* studies suggest that bioactive compounds in mushrooms have immunomodulatory, anti-inflammatory, anti-oxidative, lipid lowering and anti-tumor effects. Some research findings suggest that edible mushroom consumption is associated with prevention of cardiovascular diseases. Many of these health benefits can be attributed to the nutrient profile of the mushrooms, which include protein, B-vitamins, minerals, along with low fat content. In addition, bioactive compounds like polyphenols and flavonoids present in mushrooms may contribute to health benefits.

Weight management is a growing concern for all segments of the U.S. population. Moreover, recent statistics provide compelling evidence that overweight and obesity are on the rise not only among adults, but also in children younger than twelve years of age. This growing trend in overweight and obesity imposes major health, economic and social burdens worldwide. While genetic, biologic and social factors are responsible to a great extent, many individuals engage in dietary behaviors that put them at risk of weight gain.

On the intake side of the energy balance equation, high intake of energy-dense foods is largely responsible for the problem of positive energy balance, and the resulting epidemic of overweight and obesity in the U.S. Energy regulation is complex, but there is evidence that humans have limited ability to regulate food intake in response to changes in energy density. One obvious method of preventing passive overconsumption when consuming energy dense foods is substitution of low energy dense foods. However, palatability differences, access, cost, and habit may prevent people from choosing such foods.

Edible mushrooms are very low in calories and energy density. They have a nutrient profile similar to that of many foods recommended in weight loss/maintenance diets. However many "diet" foods have low palatability, which may result in non-adherence to these foods by those seeking to lose weight and keep it off. In contrast, edible mushrooms are generally regarded by adults as highly palatable, making them potentially a good substitute for high energy density foods in the prevention and treatment of obesity. In support of this hypothesis, one study we conducted in humans on the effect of mushroom on satiety and palatability showed promising results, suggesting a potential role in improving weight regulation. In addition, mushrooms may have the added benefit of reducing oxidative stress and inflammation, conditions that are associated with obesity and a number of chronic diseases. Future research is needed on the effect of mushroom intake on body weight regulation, and associated health benefits.

In: Food Science Research … Volume 1
Editor: Lucille Monaco Cacioppo

ISBN: 978-1-63117-932-7
© 2014 Nova Science Publishers, Inc.

Chapter 68

CULTIVATED MUSHROOMS: DISEASE CONTROL IN MUSHROOM INDUSTRY

Ivana Potočnik[*]

Institute of Pesticides and Environmental Protection,
Banatska 31B, Belgrade-Zemun, Serbia

RESEARCH SUMMARY

Button mushroom (Agaricus bisporus), oyster mushroom (*Pleurotus* sp.) and shii-take (*Lentinus edodes*) are the most commonly cultivated basidiomycetes worldwide. The production of fruiting bodies is severely afflicted by fungal, bacterial, and viral pathogens that can cause diseases which have an effect on yield and quality. Major *A. bisporus* fungal pathogens are *Mycogone perniciosa*, *Lecanicillium fungicola*, and *Cladobotryum* with two species mycophillum and dendroides, causal agents of dry bubble, wet bubble, and cobweb disease, respectively. Various *Trichoderma* species are the causal organisms of green mould, affecting all three edible mushrooms. The usual method of controlling of diseases on farms worldwide is based on the use of fungicides. However, development of pathogen resistance to fungicides after frequent application and host sensitivity to fungicides are serious problems. For improvement of crop protection and reduction of production costs, the effects of some new fungicides are being tested. The strains of edible mushrooms that were recently commonly cultivated seem to be more tolerant to fungicides in vitro than the earlier commercial strains. Resistance to benzimidazole fungicides has developed and the number of available fungicides is decreasing. Since studies of fungicides efficacy on cultivated mushrooms by agrochemical companies are very rare, only few fungicides are officially recommended in mushroom industry: prochloraz in EU countries, and chlorothalonil, thiabendazol and tiophanate-methyl in US and Canada. Decreased sensitivity of *L. fungicola* to prochloraz was noted. Also, inefficiency of this fungicide was recorded in experimental growing room, at a level of spotting symptoms of cobweb disease. However, with regard to resistance development, harm to the environment and human health, special attention should

---

[*] Tel./fax: ++381(11)3076-133 E-mail: ivanapotocnik@yahoo.com

be focused on good programme of hygiene. The introduction of new fungicides of biological origin creates new possibilities for crop protection from fungal pathogens.

In: Food Science Research ... Volume 1
Editor: Lucille Monaco Cacioppo

ISBN: 978-1-63117-932-7
© 2014 Nova Science Publishers, Inc.

Chapter 69

PRODUCTION OF *PLEUROTUS OSTREATUS* (OYSTER MUSHROOM) GROWN ON SUGAR CANE BIOMASS (TRASH, BAGASSE AND PITH)

Noé Aguilar-Rivera[*], *Adolfo Castillo Moran, Daniel Arturo Rodríguez Lagunes and Joaquín Murguia Gonzalez*

Universidad Veracruzana, Facultad de Ciencias Biológicas y Agropecuarias, Km. 1
Carretera Peñuela Amatlan de los Reyes S/N. C.P., Córdoba, Veracruz México

RESEARCH SUMMARY

Mushroom culture is a biotechnological process that recycles ligninocellulosic wastes and can be produced on natural materials from agriculture, woodland, animal husbandry, and manufacturing industries and the spent substrates can be used in different ways (soil conditioner, compost, cattle feed). Edible mushrooms are highly appreciated and have a commercial potential in many countries. They have a chemical composition, which is attractive from the nutritional point of view for protein. Mushroom yields and biological efficiency vary according to biological factors, environmental conditions and growing substrates.

Mushroom cultivation is a well-established and profitable agribusiness carried out worldwide on a large or small scale. Cultivation on sugarcane substrates is an option to be considered due to low cost as substrate, physic-chemical structure, and their positive economical, social and environmental factors for the sugarcane cultivation areas in a sugarcane diversification concept in comparison with other agricultural by-products. However, successful technology transfer programs to increase yields and reduce production costs of edible mushrooms are limited. The sustainable model for production of edible mushrooms represents a strategy that allows large-scale, small-scale, and domestic cultivation to promote regional development.

---

[*] Tel./Fax: (01) 271 71 6 73 92
Email: naguilar@uv.mx

This article discusses the development of an agro-industry of fresh and dried edible mushrooms with sugarcane production, major fundamental technologies involved: Spawn technology, Mushroom production technology, and processing technology and how their economic and nutritional potentials will increase the productivity of mushrooms on sugarcane substrates with better flavor, appearance, texture, nutritional qualities at low cost.

In: Food Science Research … Volume 1
Editor: Lucille Monaco Cacioppo

ISBN: 978-1-63117-932-7
© 2014 Nova Science Publishers, Inc.

Chapter 70

SUSTAINABLE USE OF MICROBIAL ENDOPHYTES

*Devendra Kumar Choudhary**

Department of Science, Faculty of Arts, Science & Commerce (FASC),
Mody Institute of Science & technology (MITS), Lakshmangarh-332311,
Sikar (Rajasthan), INDIA

RESEARCH SUMMARY

In the past two decades, a great deal of information on the potential role of endophytes in nature has been collected. Endophytes, microorganisms that colonize internal host tissues of living plants are a relatively unstudied and dependable source of bioactive and chemically novel compounds with potential for exploitation in a wide variety of medical and pharmacological areas. The mechanism through which endophytes exist and respond to their surroundings must be better understood. In most cases their relationship with the host plant is symbiotic and probably mutualistic. Many are capable of synthesizing bio-active compounds that can be used by the plant for defense against pathogenic fungi and bacteria. Some of these compounds have proven useful for novel drug discovery. The opportunity to find new and interesting endophytes among myriad plants is great. Endophytes represent a huge diversity of microbial adaptations that have developed in special and sequestered environments, and their diversity and specialized habituation make them an exciting field of study in the search for new medicines. The hunt for new drugs is particularly important in view of the fact that so many diseases are developing immunity to some of the current treatments. This review will concentrate on what has been discovered, and what is still unknown about endophytes that synthesize chemicals with bioactive properties.

---

* For Correspondence: Department of Science, Faculty of Arts, Science & Commerce (FASC), Mody Institute of Science & technology (MITS), Lakshmangarh-332311, Sikar (Rajasthan), INDIA E-mail: devmicro@rediffmail.com

In: Food Science Research ... Volume 1
Editor: Lucille Monaco Cacioppo

ISBN: 978-1-63117-932-7
© 2014 Nova Science Publishers, Inc.

Chapter 71

CHEMICAL COMPOSITION AND NUTRITIONAL VALUE OF EUROPEAN SPECIES OF WILD GROWING MUSHROOMS

Pavel Kalač[*]

Department of Applied Chemistry, Faculty of Agriculture, University of South Bohemia,
České Budějovice, Czech Republic

RESEARCH SUMMARY

Tens of wild growing mushroom species are widely consumed as a delicacy in a part of Europe. Knowledge of their nutritional value has so far been fragmentary mainly due to the very limited information on the bioavailability of their constituents. Dry matter content varies usually between 80 and 140 g kg[-1]. Usual medians of crude protein, lipid and ash content are about 25, 3 and 8 g per 100 g of dry matter, respectively. Various carbohydrates form the rest. However, great variations occur. Energy is low, about 150 kJ per 100 g of fresh mushrooms. The proportion of essential amino acids seems to be nutritionally favorable, while the content of n-3 fatty acids is negligible. Chitin, glycogen, mannitol and trehalose are typical carbohydrate constituents. Potassium is the highly prevailing element within minerals. Relatively high proportion of fiber, health-promoting β-glucans, compounds with antioxidation activity and flavor constituents are the topics provoking an increasing interest of both researchers and consumers. Nevertheless, several popular species accumulate high levels of cadmium, mercury and lead if growing on heavily polluted soils.

[*] E-mail: kalac@zf.jcu.cz; Phone: +420 387 772 657; Fax: +420 385 310405.

In: Food Science Research ... Volume 1
Editor: Lucille Monaco Cacioppo

ISBN: 978-1-63117-932-7
© 2014 Nova Science Publishers, Inc.

Chapter 72

PLEURAN: IMMUNOMODULOTOR POLYSACCHARIDE FROM *PLEUROTUS OSTREATUS*, STRUCTURE, PRODUCTION AND APPLICATION

Hesham El Enshasy[1,2], Parisa Maftoun[1] and Roslinda Abd Malek[1]*

[1]Institute of Bioproducts Development (IBD),
Universiti Teknologi Malaysia (UTM), Johor, Malaysia
[2]Mubarak City for Scientific Research and Technology Applications (MuCSAT),
New Burg Al Arab, Alexandria, Egypt

RESEARCH SUMMARY

Traditionally mushrooms are considered in daily diet, especially in the orient as they are rich in nutrition and have abundant therapeutic properties. Nowadays large scale mushroom cultivation takes attention of many pharmaceutical companies around the world due to their rich and variety of medicinal compounds. Extensive research in isolation, characterization and production of these biological components is conducted in last decades. Among them numerous studies are dedicated to polysaccharide production as they exhibit immunomodulator and anti-tumor activities. Glucan with different active unit linkage such as $(1\rightarrow3)$, $(1\rightarrow6)$-β-glucan and $(1\rightarrow3)$-α- glucans constitute mushroom polysaccharides which perform immunomodultor activity as they are biological response modifiers (BRMs). Beta-glucan obtained from the *Pleurotus ostreatus* (Oyster mushroom) is known in the scientific literature as pleuran. It is structural cell wall compound. It stimulates the body´s defense system against infections (bacterial, viral, yeast, and parasitic) and modulates the blood producing activity of bone marrow. In this chapter we are going to focus on the structure of pleuran, followed by its production strategies. Furthermore the therapeutic application of pleuran will be demonstrate and are for further researched will be suggested.

In: Food Science Research ... Volume 1
Editor: Lucille Monaco Cacioppo

ISBN: 978-1-63117-932-7
© 2014 Nova Science Publishers, Inc.

Chapter 73

ENHANCING THE MEDICINAL PROPERTIES OF *AGARICUS SUBRUFESCENS* BY GROWING PRACTICES

Diego Cunha Zied[1], Francisco José Gea Alegría[2] and Arturo Pardo Giménez[2]*

[1] Faculdade de Ciências Agronômicas, Universidade Estadual Paulista, Módulo de Cogumelos, Departamento de Produção Vegetal (Defesa Fitossanitária), Brazil
[2] Centro de Investigación, Experimentación y Servicios del Champiñón (CIES), Quintanar del Rey, Cuenca, Spain

RESEARCH SUMMARY

The *Agaricus subrefescens* Peck [*A. blazei* (Murrill) ss. Heinemann] mushroom has been widely studied in various parts of the world, due to its medical and pharmacological properties. As substances of interest, the cell wall of the fungi contains polysaccharides called β-glucans, which have a structural function. During the 1980s, the *A. subrufescens* mushroom was imported to Japan due to its alleged health effects and is widely used today in Oriental countries both as an edible mushroom, considered a functional food, and as a natural therapy in the form of a medicinal extract, used mostly for the prevention and treatment of cancer. In accordance with Brazilian tradition, it could be useful against a variety of diseases, such as diabetes, atherosclerosis, hepatitis, hypercholesterolemia and heart disease, among others. The mushroom is commercialized in several countries as a nutraceutical product, which is a novel class of dietary supplements, including partially refined extract or dried biomass from the mushroom made into a capsule or tablet. In general, the compositional analysis of *A. subrufescens* mushrooms is water (84-87%), protein (30-33%), fat (0.82-1.3%), fiber (5.6-6.8%) and minerals (5.9-7.1%), with β-glucan contents between 4.4 and 6.9 g 100 g^{-1} of mushroom. Active metabolites can be isolated from basidiomes; pure culture mycelia, culture filtrate, and currently numerous attempts are in progress to obtain active metabolites from the

* Faculdade de Ciências Agronômicas, Universidade Estadual Paulista, FCA/UNESP. Módulo de Cogumelos, Departamento de Produção Vegetal (Defesa Fitossanitária), Brazil. E-mail: dczied@gmail.com

mycelia through submerged fermentation culture due the cheaper preparations. The first separation of active anticancer compounds purified from the sodium hydroxide extract of the fruit body occurred in 1989. Following this achievement, several controversies have arisen, mainly regarding the nutraceutical quality of the extracts obtained and in relation to the tests conducted, emphasizing that the chemical composition and the stage of maturity of the mushrooms, as well as the cultivation practices used in growing them, are crucial to obtaining quality basidiomes with high concentrations of β-glucans. Thus, in this book chapter, the problems arising from the variability of the content of β-glucans of mushrooms due to different practices and growing techniques adopted for the *A. subrufescens* production are discussed. To achieve this, five strains (ABL 99/28, ABL 99/30, ABL 03/44, ABL 04/49 and ABL 06/59), cultivated in three composts (Massai straw + sugar cane bagasse, oat straw + sugar cane bagasse and Aruana straw + sugar cane bagasse), with four casing layers (soil + charcoal, soil + coconut fiber, soil + peat moss and soil + composted pine bark) in four growing environments (climatized chamber, greenhouse with a transparent plastic film, greenhouse with a milky-white plastic film and greenhouse with a Duplalon® plastic film) were studied, with the aim of analyzing the variability of β-glucan content in the harvested mushroom and the agronomic performance of the growing practices. The ABL 04/49 strain cultivated with Massai straw and sugar cane bagasse showed the highest concentrations of β-glucans, but not a best yield, which was achieved by the ABL 99/30 strain cultivated with oat straw + sugar cane bagasse and obtained good β-glucan content and high yield. For agronomic performance, soil + composted pine bark was highlighted, influenced by the cultivation environment, to achieve high yield. Finally, following the presentation of a series of results, the creation of a growing protocol is suggested, which seeks to adopt cultivation practices that enhance the presence of β-glucans in the mushrooms.

In: Food Science Research ... Volume 1
Editor: Lucille Monaco Cacioppo

ISBN: 978-1-63117-932-7
© 2014 Nova Science Publishers, Inc.

Chapter 74

HEMOLYTIC LECTINS OF HIGHER MUSHROOMS

V. O. Antonyuk and R. S. Stoika

Institute of Cell Biology National Academy of Sciences of Ukraine, Ukraine

RESEARCH SUMMARY

The results of study of 4 specific lectins isolated from higher *Amanita* genus mushrooms and possessing hemolytic activity are presented. Two of them – *A. phalloides and A. virosa*, belong to *Amanitaceae* family, while two others - *Mycena pura* and *Laetiporus sulphureus*, belong to *Tricholomataceae* and *Corticiaceae* families, correspondingly. The purification methods used for their isolation are described, and the comparative analysis of physico-chemical and biological properties of these lectins have been done. It was shown that according to the peculiarities of the action towards erythrocytes, these lectins can be divided into two groups. While in *Mycena pura* and *Laetiporus sulphureus* lectins, the hemagglutinating activity is higher than the hemolytic activity, in *A. virosa* and *A. phalloides* lectins, situation is opposite and the hemolytic activity is higher than the hemagglutinating activity. The hemolytic activity of the lectins under study was inhibited by the polyethylene glycol of high molecular mass. At the same time, the presence of polyethylene glycol did not influence the hemagglutinating ability of the lectins. This allowed studying their carbohydrate specificity, and it was found that the lectins of *Amanita* genus mushrooms considerably differed in this specificity. The hemolytic lectins also possessed antimicrobial action and inhibited growth of Gram-positive microorganisms and *Proteus*. Besides, they demonstrated cytotoxic action towards cultured mammalian leukemia cells. In general, these mushroom lectins resemble cytolytic lectins of lower invertebrates. Their potential biological role is considered.

In: Food Science Research ... Volume 1
Editor: Lucille Monaco Cacioppo

ISBN: 978-1-63117-932-7
© 2014 Nova Science Publishers, Inc.

Chapter 75

RADIOACTIVITY OF EUROPEAN WILD GROWING EDIBLE MUSHROOMS

Pavel Kalač[*]

Department of Applied Chemistry, Faculty of Agriculture, University of South Bohemia,
CZ-37005 České Budějovice, Czech Republic

RESEARCH SUMMARY

Wild growing mushrooms are widely consumed as a delicacy in several European countries, at level up to several kg per year per capita. Activity concentrations of the natural isotope ^{40}K are usually 800-1,500 Bq kg^{-1} dry matter (DM). Other natural radionuclides with leading ^{210}Pb and ^{210}Po are of lower importance. Activities of ^{137}Cs from nuclear weapons testing below 1,000 Bq kg^{-1} DM were commonly reported until 1986. The situation changed dramatically after the accident of Chernobyl nuclear power station in 1986. Activities up to over 100,000 Bq kg^{-1} DM of ^{137}Cs and to a lesser extent of ^{134}Cs were observed in some edible species in the following years. Commonly, mycorrhizal species accumulate radiocesium more than species with saprotrophic or parasitic nutritional strategy. *Xerocomus badius, X. chrysenteron, Suillus variegatus, Rozites caperata, Laccaria amethystina* and *Hydnum repandum* belong among the radiocesium highly accumulating and widely consumed species. Activity concentrations have been affected by several environmental factors, such as rate of soil contamination by the Chernobyl fallout, the depth from which mycelium takes nutrients and time since the accident. Most of the ^{137}Cs in forest soils appear to be available for uptake by mushrooms until now. A considerable consumption of accumulating species collected from the sites heavily contaminated in 1986 can be still of a health concern. The contamination can be reduced by soaking or cooking of dried or frozen mushroom slices. Until now, meat of wild boars eating some mushroom species from heavily contaminated areas can highly surpass statutory limit for ^{137}Cs.

[*] E-mail: kalac@zf.jcu.cz; Phone: +420 387 772 657; Fax: +420 385 310405

In: Food Science Research ... Volume 1
Editor: Lucille Monaco Cacioppo

ISBN: 978-1-63117-932-7
© 2014 Nova Science Publishers, Inc.

Chapter 76

WHITE BUTTON MUSHROOMS, QUALITY EVALUATION AND SHELF LIFE PREDICTION

Masoud Taghizadeh[1], Aoife Gowen[2] and Colm O'Donnell[2]
[1] Ferdowsi University of Mashhad (FUM)
[2] University College Dublin (UCD)

RESEARCH SUMMARY

White button mushroom (*Agaricus bisporus*) is the most commonly cultivated mushroom species which comprises about 32% of world mushroom production. It is a good source of proteins, amino acids, carbohydrates, vitamins (mainly vitamin D and vitamin B-complex) and minerals, such as iron, calcium, phosphorous and potassium. *Agaricus bisporus* mushroom is valued for its white appearance and browning of its cap is an indicator of poor quality. Browning and bruising of the mushroom surface lead to reduced shelf-life and lower financial returns to producers, therefore there is a need for objective evaluation of mushroom quality to ensure that only high quality produce reaches the market. Traditional methods have been widely used to evaluate mushroom quality and shelf life based on several quality parameters such as visual appearance, size, colour, maturity stage, development stage, microbial growth and weight loss. However, today's mushroom industry demands non-destructive, rapid and accurate on-line sensor technologies to monitor and control mushroom quality and safety. In this chapter, some traditional quality grading methods as well as application of novel techniques for mushroom quality and shelf life evaluation are discussed.

In: Food Science Research ... Volume 1
Editor: Lucille Monaco Cacioppo

ISBN: 978-1-63117-932-7
© 2014 Nova Science Publishers, Inc.

Chapter 77

BASIDIOMYCETES MUSHROOMS OF BRAZILIAN TROPICAL RAINFORESTS: BIODIVERSITY AND BIOLOGICAL APPLICATIONS

Luiz H. Rosa[1], Susana Johann[1], Carlos L. Zani[2], and Carlos A. Rosa[1]

[1]Departamento de Microbiologia, Instituto de Ciências Biológicas, Universidade Federal de Minas Gerais, Belo Horizonte, MG, Brazil
[2]Laboratório de Química de Produtos Naturais, Centro de Pesquisas René Rachou, Fundação Oswaldo Cruz, Belo Horizonte, MG, Brazil

RESEARCH SUMMARY

Basidiomycetes mushrooms comprise a diversity of gill fungi that occur in most terrestrial ecosystems worldwide. However, data about their diversity and biological applications in tropical ecosystems remain almost unknown. Some *Basidiomycetes* species from Brazilian tropical rainforests have been described as sources of primary and secondary bioactive compounds with antimicrobial, anti-inflammatory, immunomodulatory, antiparasitic, and antitumoral metabolites and as nutraceutical foods. In addition, some *Basidiomycetes* have demonstrated potential as producers of interesting prototype molecules for the development of drugs useful in medicine. The purpose of the present chapter will be to summarize the current status of the diversity, biotechnological use, and ability to produce different bioactive compounds of *Basidiomycetes* mushrooms from Brazilian tropical rainforests.

In: Food Science Research ... Volume 1
Editor: Lucille Monaco Cacioppo

ISBN: 978-1-63117-932-7
© 2014 Nova Science Publishers, Inc.

Chapter 78

CO-CULTIVATION OF *PLEUROTUS* SPECIES WITH YEASTS

D. N. Novoselova and O. V. Kamzolkina[*1]
[1]Mycology and Algology Department, Biological Faculty,
Lomonosov MSU, Moscow. Russia

RESEARCH SUMMARY

Fungi of the genus *Pleurotus* are one of the most popular edible fungi in the world. Most of the cultivation substrates and wood too is very poor in nitrogen, so one of the greatest problems for all wood decay fungi including *Pleurotus* species is to provide themselves nitrogen nutrition. To satisfy their nitrogen requirement *Pleurotus* fungi can parasitize on the bacteria, yeasts, and algae cells in nature and during the cultivation process.

Some of the wide cultivated *Pleurotus* species (*P. citrinopileatus*, *P. djamor*, *P. eryngii*, *P. ostreatus*, and *P. pulmonarius*) were observed in mixed cultures with 8 species (10 strains) of yeasts from different taxonomic groups (ascomycetous, i.e. *Debaryomyces hansenii*, *Hanseniaspora uvarum*, *Kluyveromyces marxianus*, *Metschnikowia pulcherrima*, *Saccharomyces cerevisiae*, and basidiomycetous, i.e. *Cryptococcus albidus*, *Cystofilobasidium capitatum, Rhodotorula minuta*) on agar media. To provide co-cultivation on agar media and on substrate were used water suspension of alive or dead yeast cells, or the suspension supernatant.

The morphological and physiological peculiarities of *Pleurotus* mycelium were described on agar medium in mixed cultures with the suspension of alive/dead yeast cells. Some specialized mycelial structures were found only in the mixed cultures with yeasts, and weren't found in the pure culture, e.g. short nipple-like appendages and coralloid hyphae, which provide contacts between mycelium and yeast cells.

The trophic preferendum was defined for each of five *Pleurotus* species, and then *Pleurotus* fungi were cultivated on substrate in association with the yeast species from the range of trophic preferendum. On substrate all five *Pleurotus* species demonstrated the same

[*] Email: o-kamzolkina@yandex.ru

reaction on the yeast cells presence. Mycelium growth speed was higher on substrate with yeast suspension. Biomass of the fruiting bodies was higher for different species, and the highest increase was shown for *P. eryngii*, twofold in comparison with the biomass of the fruiting bodies which grew on the substrate without yeasts. Analyses of amino acids and volatile compounds of *P. citrinopileatus* fruiting bodies, cultivated with and without yeast *S. cerevisiae*, demonstated high food value and wide spectrum of odor.

In: Food Science Research ... Volume 1
Editor: Lucille Monaco Cacioppo

ISBN: 978-1-63117-932-7
© 2014 Nova Science Publishers, Inc.

Chapter 79

ANTIOXIDANT PROPERTIES OF THE MOST COMMON EDIBLE MUSHROOMS CONSUMED IN BRAZIL

Gisele Pezente Ferrari, Andréia Assunção Soares,
Gisele Cristina dos Santos Bazanella, Adelar Bracht,
Cristina Giatti Marques de Souza, Cinthia Gandolfi Bôer
and Rosane Marina Peralta[*]
Departamento de Bioquímica, Universidade Estadual de Maringá,
Maringá, PR, Brazil

RESEARCH SUMMARY

Mushrooms are functional foods largely consumed in Asia and Europe. The consumption of mushroom in Brazil is very low, in part due to the lack of information about the nutritional value of the edible mushrooms cultivated in the country. The objective of this chapter was to investigate the antioxidant properties and to quantify the phenolic contents of hydroalcoholic extracts of the most commonly mushrooms consumed in Brazil: *Agaricus bisporus* (white button mushroom), *Lentinula edodes* (shiitake), *Pleurotus ostreatus* (shimeji) and *Pleurotus eryngii* (eryngii). Among four edible mushrooms studied, *A. bisporus* presented the highest phenolic contents (19.97±2.01 mg/g dry extract), followed by *P. ostreatus* (16.05±1.10 mg/g), *P. eryngii* (12.74±0.98 mg/g) and *L. edodes* (10.00±0.76 mg/g). The antioxidant activities were evaluated using four methods. A strong correlation was found between the phenolic contents and the antioxidant activity determined by the scavenging activity of DPPH radicals, reducing power and lipid peroxidation inhibition. On the other hand, a weak correlation was found between the phenolic content and the chelating activity against Fe^{2+}. The results obtained allow to conclude that the mushrooms produced in Brazil present antioxidant properties, and that the most popular of them, *A. bisporus*, appears as an excellent option to enrich the diet with antioxidant phenolic compounds.

[*] E-mail: rmperalta@uem.br, rosanemperalta@gmail.com; Phone: 554430114715

In: Food Science Research ... Volume 1
Editor: Lucille Monaco Cacioppo

ISBN: 978-1-63117-932-7
© 2014 Nova Science Publishers, Inc.

Chapter 80

BIOLOGICALLY ACTIVE MUSHROOM PROTEINS

T. B. Ng and Xiu Juan Ye*

School of Biomedical Sciences, Faculty of Medicine,
Chinese University of Hong Kong, Shatin
New Territories, Hong Kong, China

RESEARCH SUMMARY

The objective of this article is to review mushroom proteins with biological activity. They include antifungal proteins, antibacterial proteins, ribosome inactivating proteins, ribonucleases, ubiquitin- like proteins, lectins, proteases, hemolysins, laccases, xylanases, acid phosphatases, L-amino acid oxidases, α -mannosidases, deoxyribonucleases, carboxylesterases, polysaccharopeptides and polysaccharoproteins, amatoxins, phallotoxins and virotoxins.

* Corresponding author: T.B. Ng,Email: b021770@mailserv.cuhk.edu.hk;,Fax: +852-2603-5123; Phone: +852-2609-6872

In: Food Science Research … Volume 1
Editor: Lucille Monaco Cacioppo

ISBN: 978-1-63117-932-7
© 2014 Nova Science Publishers, Inc.

Chapter 81

MEDICINAL ACTIVITIES OF MUSHROOM POLYSACCHROPEPTIDES

Tzi Bun Ng[*], Jack Ho Wong[*], Helen Chan, Tak Fu Tse and Timothy Tam

Chinese University of Hong Kong, Satin, New Territories, Hong Kong, China
and Vita Green Pharmaceutical (H.K.) Limited, Hong Kong, China

RESEARCH SUMMARY

Mushrooms produce a number of molecules with medicinal properties, including polysaccharides, polysaccharide-peptide complexes, lectins, and antifungal proteins have been isolated from several mushroom species, but the one from *Coriolus versicolor* designated as PSP is the most extensively studied. PSP induces apoptosis in a variety of tumor cells by regulating the expression of pro- and anti-apoptotic genes.. It inhibits angiogenesis, regulates the production of cytokines, counteracts the action of immunosuppressive agents, and potentiates the action of antitumor drugs. PSP is devoid of toxicity on female reproductive physiology and embryonic development. Polysaccharide-peptide complexes from other mushroom species also manifest antitumor and immunoregulatory activities.

[*] Corresponding authors: School of Biomedical Sciences, Faculty of Medicine, The Chinese University of Hong Kong, Satin, New Territories, Hong Kong, China and Vita Green Pharmaceutical (H.K.) Limited, 15th floor, Oceanic Industrial Centre, 2 Lee Lok Street, Ap Lei Chau, Hong Kong, China.

In: Food Science Research … Volume 1
Editor: Lucille Monaco Cacioppo

ISBN: 978-1-63117-932-7
© 2014 Nova Science Publishers, Inc.

Chapter 82

ACTIVATION AND STABILIZATION OF MUSHROOM TYROSINASE BY ADDITION OF POLYETHYLENE GLYCOLS

Zhen Yang, Ya-Jun Yue and Ting-Wei Chen*

College of Life Sciences, Shenzhen University, Shenzhen, China

RESEARCH SUMMARY

Effect of polyethylene glycol (PEG) and its molecular weight on the activity and stability of mushroom tyrosinase was studied systematically. The kinetic parameters (such as K_m, V_{max}, optimal pH and temperature, and activation energy) and the thermostability of the enzyme at different temperatures were determined and compared in the aqueous solution with and without addition of PEGs. Polyethylene glycol showed the ability of both activating and stabilizing the enzyme (e.g., a 1.6-fold increase in V_{max}/K_m and a 1.8-fold increase in $t_{1/2}$ were achieved in the presence of PEG 10000), and such PEG-induced activation and stabilization effect was molecular weight dependent. Both our activity and stability data suggest that PEG can affect the enzyme activity and stability basically via its interaction with the enzyme so as to modify the enzyme's active site and conformation or steric structure.

---

* Corresponding author: Dr. Zhen Yang; College of Life Sciences, Shenzhen University, Shenzhen 518060, China
Email: zyang@szu.edu.cn;

In: Food Science Research … Volume 1
Editor: Lucille Monaco Cacioppo

ISBN: 978-1-63117-932-7
© 2014 Nova Science Publishers, Inc.

Chapter 83

AGARICUS BM MUSHROOM MAY PROTECT ATHLETES AGAINST INFLAMMATION, INFECTION AND ASTHMA

G. Hetland[*]

Dept. of Cellular Therapy, Oslo University Hospital, Oslo, Norway

RESEARCH SUMMARY

Athletes are known to be prone to illnesses such as infection and asthma, which is due to exercise-related skewness of the immune response, and injury-related inflammation in the muscle-skeleton system. The Brazilian medicinal mushroom, *Agaricus blazei* Murill (AbM), has strong immunomodulatory properties and is shown to protect against infections, allergy and asthma in animal models. An AbM-based extract (AndoSan[TM]) is also found to have anti-inflammatory effect both in healthy individuals and in patients with inflammatory bowel diseases. Hence, it is suggested that AbM mushroom extract may be beneficial for athletes during strenuous exercise.

[*] Correspondence: Geir Hetland, MD, PhD, Dept. of Cellular Therapy, Oslo University Hospital, Ullernchausseen 70, 0310 Oslo, Norway, E-mail: geir.hetland@rikshospitalet.no

In: Food Science Research ... Volume 1
Editor: Lucille Monaco Cacioppo

ISBN: 978-1-63117-932-7
© 2014 Nova Science Publishers, Inc.

Chapter 84

BIOLOGICAL ACTIVITIES OF *PLEUROTUS* MUSHROOMS

D. T. U. Abeytunga

Department of Chemistry, University of Colombo, Sri Lanka

RESEARCH SUMMARY

Pleurotus mushrooms are popular edible mushrooms all over the world. Studies on this genus have shown that these mushrooms possess anticancer, antimicrobial, antiviral, antioxidant, antinociceptive, antidiabetic activities and cholesterol lowering properties. Proteins, enzymes, polysaccharides such as glucans, and glycoproteins isolated from *Pleurotus* mushrooms are responsible for the said activities. Proteins such as ubiquitins, hemolysins and lectins have shown antiviral activity. It is noteworthy, that anti-HIV activity was observed in all 3 classes of aforementioned proteins. Lignolytic enzymes such as laccases present in *Pleurotus* have helped in converting agricultural waste to animal feed. Glucans are known to possess anticancer activity, antiviral activity and cholesterol lowering properties. Water insoluble glucans present in *Pleurotus* have been converted to water soluble carboxymethylated and sulfated glucans having antitumor and antiviral activities respectively. A few secondary plant metabolites are identified from *Pleurotus* mushrooms such as pleurotin which has promising anticancer properties and lovastain with cholesterol lowering properties. An oxidized form of the abundant fungal steroid ergosterol has shown antifungal activity while ergosterol itself was implicated in bringing about inhibition of lipid peroxidation. The total phenolic content is also positively correlated to the antioxidant activity. Carbon-8 compounds arising from the hydroperoxidation of linoleic acid present in the fruiting body, is identified as a compound responsible for the production of the pleasant aroma in the mushroom. A mixture containing such volatile compounds mimicking the concentration in the fruiting bodies has shown antibacterial activity.

In: Food Science Research ... Volume 1
Editor: Lucille Monaco Cacioppo

ISBN: 978-1-63117-932-7
© 2014 Nova Science Publishers, Inc.

Chapter 85

WINES FROM TROPICAL PLANTS: PROCESSING, MICROBIOLOGICAL, CHEMICAL AND HEALTH ASPECTS

Cheunjit Prakitchaiwattana and Kanitha Tananuwong[†]*

Department of Food Technology, Faculty of Science,
Chulalongkorn University, Phyathai Road, Pathumwan
Bangkok, Thailand

RESEARCH SUMMARY

World-class wines are generally originated from homemade production based on a local expertise inherited through generations. In general, grape is the raw material that has been used for wine production and developed to be a worldwide alcoholic beverage. However, tropical plants can also be used for wine making and have gained more interest because of the diversity of the raw materials, their uniqueness and health benefits. Indigenous/traditional wines made from tropical plants, such as rice-based wines, tropical fruit wines and herb wines can be prepared in the household or small scale industry using simple techniques and equipment. Quality and specific characteristics of these indigenous wines depend mainly upon wine maker's techniques and types of raw materials. Some of the products such as rice wine, using a mold-based system for the production, is now available worldwide and manufactured on the large scale. Meanwhile, some other rice-based wines such as red rice and even rice husk wines still have been the indigenous alcoholic beverages of the particular regions in Asia. Over the last decade, wines from some tropical fruits such as mango, orange and pineapple have been produced in an industrial scale and become well-renowned in particular countries. Many other tropical fruits which possess attractive color, aroma and taste, including longan, lychee, mangosteen, papaya, banana, tamarind and mulberry, have

* Corresponding author: Cheunjit Prakitchaiwattana, Ph.D. Assistant professor Telephone: +66 2 218 5531. Fax: +66 2 254 4314. Email: Cheunjit.p@chula.ac.th. Additional email: pcheunjit@yahoo.com.
† Kanitha Tananuwong, Ph.D. Telephone: +66 2 218 5246. Fax: +66 2 254 4314. Email: Kanitha.T@chula.ac.th Additional email: hellotafst@yahoo.com.

also been used for wine making. These unique wines are locally consumed, particularly in South East Asian countries, yet having high potential for worldwide distribution. Palm tree, a source of palm sap which is sugary juice with typically sweet aroma, is another significant tropical plant used for wine production. Palm wine is widely produced and consumed in some Asian and African countries. Medicinal plants such as tropical herbs are also used for wine making. This wine type has been recognized as an indigenous medicinal wine and widely consumed in Asian countries. It has been well recognized that the indigenous wines of each region are produced based on local techniques restrictedly known by their manufacturers for a long time. Nevertheless, many wine types, which are expansively popular, still have not received scientific attention. Many research groups have therefore tried to conduct a systematic investigation of all aspects of indigenous wines production. Results from those studies could help improve quality standards, which could match with industrial specification and needs. Therefore, different aspects of the wines from tropical plants, including (i) production process of the indigenous wines, (ii) microbiological aspects associated with fermentation quality (iii) chemical aspects associated with sensory characteristics, especially flavor and aroma, and (iv) health aspects associated with beneficial bioactive compounds and potential toxins presenting the wine, will be reviewed in this chapter.

In: Food Science Research ... Volume 1
Editor: Lucille Monaco Cacioppo

ISBN: 978-1-63117-932-7
© 2014 Nova Science Publishers, Inc.

Chapter 86

EFFECT OF WINEMAKING TECHNIQUES ON BIOACTIVE COMPOUNDS IN WHITE AND RED WINE

Giuseppe Di Lecce,[1] Sara Arranz,[2] Ramon Estruch[2,3] and Rosa M. Lamuela-Raventósa[2]*

[1]Nutrition and Food Science Department, XaRTA, INSA. Pharmacy School,
University of Barcelona, Barcelona, Spain
[2]Department of Internal Medicine, Hospital Clinic,
University of Barcelona Barcelona, Spain
[3]CIBER CB06/03 Fisiopatología de la Obesidad y la Nutrición, (CIBEROBN)
and RETICS RD, Instituto de Salud Carlos III, Spain

RESEARCH SUMMARY

The emotional and hedonistic quality of wine plays an important role in the purchase decision by the consumer, and its valorisation depends on certain controlled and desired properties, which involve both sensory and nutritional characteristics. As a consequence, the production of wines with high quality standards in terms of fine taste, enriched flavour, limited browning, high stability and also health properties is one of the focal points of interest for both winemakers and researchers.

Compared to the past, nowadays there is a greater awareness of the health implications of a moderate consumption of wine (equivalent to 2 glasses per day for men and one and a half for women), associated with a decreased incidence of cardiovascular and other chronic diseases. Indeed, *Vitis vinifera* has proven to be a rich source of a wide group of plant secondary metabolites known as polyphenols, whose biological, and functional properties have been extensively reviewed and range from vasodilatory to anticarcinogenic, anti-inflammatory, antibacterial, immune-stimulating, antiallergic, antiviral and estrogenic. Recent

* Corresponding author: Dr Rosa Maria Lamuela-Raventós. Department of Nutrition and Food Science-CeRTA, Faculty of Pharmacy, University of Barcelona, Av. Joan XXIII s/n, 08028 Barcelona, Spain. Ph: +34 934034843. Fax: +34 934035931. E-mail: lamuela@ub.edu.

evidence also suggests that flavonoids found in grapes have the capacity to improve several aspects of memory and learning.

The phenolic fingerprint of wine is affected by the grape variety, climate, growing conditions and terroir, the ripening stage and, last but not least, by winemaking variables and techniques. The latter factors play a particularly important role in determining the chemical, sensory and nutritional quality of wines and in the last twenty years innovation in winemaking technology has been oriented to maximize the recovery and preservation of natural grape components with a high nutritional value.

Grape skins, pulp and seeds contain a large amount of phenolic compounds that are partially extracted during winemaking, and the phenolic profile and content of wines is significantly affected by winemaking techniques and enological practices. Thus, to boost intake of phenolic compounds without increasing wine consumption, it is necessary to enhance their extraction during the winemaking process. Extensive research has focused on setting up new technological models to obtain wines enriched with phenolic compounds with notable benefits for health while preserving their final quality characteristics.

This chapter reviews the available literature on the impact of winemaking technology on phenolic extraction, including pre-fermentative practices, maceration and its parameters, saignée, delayed punching-down or pumping-over, termovinification and cryo-maceration, prolonged maceration skin contact and carbonic maceration. The advantages and disadvantages of the different winemaking technologies from the viewpoint of both wine quality and human health will be discussed. The aim is to provide a helpful tool for studies attempting to change the functional properties of wines by increasing their polyphenol content.

In: Food Science Research ... Volume 1
Editor: Lucille Monaco Cacioppo

ISBN: 978-1-63117-932-7
© 2014 Nova Science Publishers, Inc.

Chapter 87

MICRO-OXYGENATION OF RED WINE: CHEMISTRY AND SENSORY ASPECTS

Giuseppina Paola Parpinello and Andrea Versari[*]
Università degli Studi di Bologna, Campus of Food Science,
Cesena (FC), Italy

RESEARCH SUMMARY

Micro-oxygenation (MOX) is the process of introducing a low amount of oxygen during initial aging of red wine in the attempt to control desirable changes in its sensory properties. Although MOX can enhance the structure and colour of wine due to the reaction of phenolic compounds to form more stable polymeric structures, the reduction of astringency is less certain. It is also claimed that MOX might reduce excessively herbaceous character and reductive aroma of wine.

MOX was developed during the early 1990s and is usually applied to red wines stored in steel tanks as alternative to oak ageing. The oxygen level into the wine over the course of treatment is the critical point to control the oxidation reactions that take place. Thus, the success of the MOX relies on the ability to control the rate of oxygen dosage.

The MOX process is not well understood yet and represents one of the major controversial application of modern winemaking. The importance of oxygen level on the chemical and sensory changes of red wines is the central topic of this chapter.

---

[*] Corresponding author E-mail: andrea.versari@unibo.it.

In: Food Science Research ... Volume 1
Editor: Lucille Monaco Cacioppo

ISBN: 978-1-63117-932-7
© 2014 Nova Science Publishers, Inc.

Chapter 88

EFFECTS OF WINE CONSUMPTION ON THE CARDIOVASCULAR SYSTEM

S. Arranz,[1] G. Di Lecce,[2] R. Lamuela-Raventós[3,4] and R. Estruch[1,4,]*

[1]Department of Internal Medicine, Hospital Clinic, Institut d'Investigacions Biomédiques August Pi i Sunyer (IDIBAPS), University of Barcelona, Barcelona, Spain
[2]Dipartimento SAIFET, Sez. Scienze e Tecnologie Alimentari, Università Politecnica delle Marche, Ancona, Italy
[3]Nutrition and Food Science Department, CeRTA, INSA Pharmacy School, University of Barcelona, Av. Joan XXIII s/n Barcelona, Spain
[4]CIBEROBN Fisiopatologia de la Obesidad y la Nutrición and RETIC RD06/0045 Alimentación saludable en la prevención primaria de enfermedades crónicas: la Red Predimed. Instituto de Salud Carlos III, Spain

RESEARCH SUMMARY

Excessive alcohol consumption is associated with increased morbidity and mortality as well as with labour and traffic accidents. The medical consequences of excessive alcohol consumption include acute intoxication, alcohol dependence, liver cirrhosis, pancreatitis, hypertension, stroke, dilated cardiomyopathy, cardiac arrhythmias and sudden death.

On the other hand, humans have drunk wine since ancient times and many believe in its beneficial effects on cardiovascular system. Several epidemiological studies have pointed out that light-to-moderate alcohol consumers have an increased survival compared to abstainers. Current evidence also suggests beneficial effects of moderate drinking on cardiovascular events including coronary heart disease, ischaemic stroke, peripheral arteriopathy and congestive heart failure. Other positive effects of moderate drinking have also been reported on the quality of life, cognitive function, and dementia.

---

* E-mail: restruch@clinic.ub.es.

The underlying mechanisms to explain these protective effects against coronary heart disease include an increase in high-density lipoprotein cholesterol, a decrease in platelet aggregation, a reduction in the levels of fibrinogen and an increase in insulin sensitivity. Recently, additional beneficial effects of the intake of wine against atherosclerosis have been attributed to their antioxidant and anti-inflammatory effects, as well as their actions on vascular function. However, alcohol consumption does not produce the same effects in all patients, since some subjects, such as women or patients with some ethanol-related diseases, seem to be more sensitive to the toxic effects of alcohol. In addition, there are discrepancies regarding the specific effects of different types of beverages on the cardio-vascular system, and also whether the possible protective effects of alcoholic beverages are due to its alcohol component (ethanol) or non-alcoholic products containing, mainly polyphenols. Recent randomised clinical trials have shown that wine provides higher antioxidant and anti-inflammatory effects than some spirits (gin) due to its higher polyphenolic content. In such studies, those subjects who showed higher absorption of polyphenols showed lower serum concentration of inflammatory biomarkers than their counterparts. In addition, other studies performed in women have observed that daily doses of 15-20 g of alcohol as red wine are sufficient to elicit protective effects similar to those observed in men who consumed higher doses of wine.

In conclusion, moderate consumption of wine exerts a protective effect on biomarkers related to the progression and development of atherosclerosis due to its alcoholic (ethanol) and non-alcoholic (polyphenols) content. Women and subjects with high polyphenol absorption are more sensitive to the beneficial effects of wine.

In: Food Science Research ... Volume 1
Editor: Lucille Monaco Cacioppo

ISBN: 978-1-63117-932-7
© 2014 Nova Science Publishers, Inc.

Chapter 89

EFFECTS OF WINE ON VASCULATURE

Dimitris Tousoulis, Anna-Maria Kampoli, and Christodoulos Stefanadis*

1st Cardiology Unit, Hippokration Hospital, Athens University
Medical School, Greece

RESEARCH SUMMARY

Atherosclerosis is a chronic inflammatory disease which may cause obstructions of the coronary, cerebral and peripheral arteries. It is typically multifactorial, most often dependent on risk factors such as hypercholesterolemia, diabetes, smoking, hypertension, sedentary lifestyle, and obesity. It is the single main cause of death in most developed countries due to myocardial infarction, angina, sudden death, and heart failure. Although excessive consumption of ethanol in alcoholic beverages causes multi-organ damage, moderate consumption, particularly of red wine, is protective against all-cause mortality. Epidemiological studies suggest that consumption of wine, grape products and other foods containing polyphenols is associated with decreased risk for cardiovascular disease. The benefits of wine consumption appear to be greater than other alcoholic beverages. Experimental studies indicate that grape polyphenols could reduce atherosclerosis by a number of mechanisms, including inhibition of oxidation of LDL and other favorable effects on cellular redox state, improvement of endothelial function, lowering blood pressure, inhibition of platelet aggregation, reducing inflammation, and activating novel proteins that prevent cell senescence. All these effects of red wine might interfere with atherosclerotic plaque development and stability, vascular thrombosis and occlusion. The beneficial effects of red wine consumption in human vasculature have been also shown by the measurement of flow-mediated vasodilation (FMD) using high-resolution brachial artery ultrasonography. An improvement of FMD values to the individuals drinking red wine has been described. These findings lead to the concept that moderate red wine drinking, in the absence of

* Address of correspondence: Ass Prof Dimitris Tousoulis MD, PhD, FACC. 1st Cardiology Unit, Hippokration Hospital, Athens University Medical School, Athens, Greece. Tel: +30-210-7782446. Fax: +30-210-7784590. Email: drtousoulis@hotmail.com.

contraindications, may be beneficial to patients who are at risk of atherosclerotic cardiovascular events. Although, mounting evidence strongly supports beneficial cardiovascular effects of moderate red wine consumption in most populations, clinical advice to abstainers to initiate daily alcohol consumption has not yet been substantiated in the literature and further prospective controlled clinical studies are need to be conducted.

In: Food Science Research ... Volume 1
Editor: Lucille Monaco Cacioppo

ISBN: 978-1-63117-932-7
© 2014 Nova Science Publishers, Inc.

Chapter 90

NEW WINEMAKING PRACTICES: THE USE OF INACTIVE DRY YEAST PREPARATIONS TO IMPROVE FERMENTATION AND THE ORGANOLEPTIC CHARACTERISTICS OF WINE

Inmaculada Andujar-Ortiz,[*] M. Victoria Moreno-Arribas and M. Ángeles Pozo-Bayón
Instituto de Investigación en Ciencias de la Alimentación (CIAL) (CSIC-UAM), Nicolás Cabrera, Campus de la Universidad Autónoma de Madrid, Cantoblanco, Madrid, Spain

RESEARCH SUMMARY

Currently, the use of inactive dry yeast (IDY) preparations is gaining popularity within the oenological industry. These preparations are obtained from *Saccharomyces cerevisiae* yeast once their fermentative capacity has been eliminated, in general by autolysis. They include in their composition, soluble (amino acids, peptides, monosaccharide, etc.) and insoluble compounds (yeast membranes and walls), which are responsible for multiple effects noticed in the wines. Although traditionally, they have been mainly used for the improvement of alcoholic and malolactic fermentation, new applications based on their use for enhancing wine's sensory characteristics, are being proposed. As a matter of fact, it has been shown that glycoproteins present in these preparations are able to protect wine colour, because of their interaction with tannins and anthocyanins, therefore, avoiding or minimising polyphenol aggregation and precipitation. In addition, some yeast macromolecules released from IDY may affect the volatility of important wine aroma compounds which could be related to the sensory differences observed in wines supplemented with these preparations. Moreover, the ability of IDY to release nitrogen heterocyclic volatile compounds, likely formed as a consequence of the thermal reactions accounted for in the last steps during their production

---

[*] Tel. 0034910017900. Fax 0034910017905.

has been also shown. Other types of IDYs, which have been claimed to preserve aroma composition during wine storage, have been associated to the presence of a large amount of glutathione (GSH). On the other hand, the use of these preparations might have also negative consequences on wine's sensory characteristics (adsorption of volatile or anthocyanic compounds).

In general, although some of these preparations have very specific applications and there are currently many of these products in the market under different brands that promise different ways for improving wine characteristics, the scientific information about the chemistry beyond their use and their action mode is still scarce. The objective of this chapter, is therefore, to review the different applications of specific IDY preparations in winemaking, on the basis of their action mechanisms taking into consideration the scientific information available, underlining the necessity of more scientific work in order to better characterize their chemical composition, their action mechanisms, and the establishment of better criteria for their oenological use.

In: Food Science Research ... Volume 1
Editor: Lucille Monaco Cacioppo

ISBN: 978-1-63117-932-7
© 2014 Nova Science Publishers, Inc.

Chapter 91

ANALYTICAL METHODS FOR THE DETECTION OF OCHRATOXIN A IN WINES

Akhtar Hayat and Lise Barthelmebs[*]
IMAGES, Batiment S, Université de Perpignan,
Perpignan Cedex, France

RESEARCH SUMMARY

Ochratoxin A (OTA), a mycotoxin produced by various *Aspergillus* and *Penicillium* strains under diverse environmental conditions, has been found as a common contaminant of wide variety of cereals (wheat, barley, maize, oats), dried fruits, spices, coffee and fermented beverages. OTA has been classified by the IARC (International Agency for Research on Cancer) as a possible carcinogen to humans (Group 2B) due to its widespread on such a large variety of agricultural commodities and the potential health risks, mainly towards humans. Recent studies have shown that in the European diet, wine has been identified as the second major source of human exposure to OTA, following cereals. The European Food Safety Authority has also set a maximum level of OTA in wine (red, white and rosé) and other wine and/or grape must based beverages of 2 µg/kg. Accurate and sensitive determination of this carcinogenic compound became an important requirement to meet wine safety concerns and official legislated regulations. For these reasons, analytical methods for OTA continued to develop over the decades, reflecting advances in analytical chemistry. Chromatographic techniques, mainly based on liquid chromatography with fluorescence or mass detection, coupled with immunoaffinity column (IACs) or solid phase extraction clean-up, have been validated and adopted as official analytical methods for OTA determination in wine. Enzyme-linked immunosorbent assays (ELISA) are well suited for specific and relative inexpensive screening of OTA in wine. Recently, novel technologies using antibodies against OTA have been proposed and include lateral flow devices, flow-through enzyme immunoassays, fluorescence polarization immunoassays and immunosensors. Although immunoassay

---

[*] Corresponding author: Phone : +33 468 66 22 56, Fax : +33 468 66 22 23, E-mail address: barthelm@univ-perp.fr.

methods exhibit high sensitivity and acceptable performances allowing the detection of OTA at concentrations equal or lower than the regulatory values, these methods require a stable source of antibodies, mainly achieved from commercial sources. Chemically synthesized counterparts to natural antibodies in the form of aptamers seem a promising alternative for the development of analytical methods. This new class of molecules has already been used in bioanalytical methods for OTA detection, in electrochemical and optical techniques. In this chapter, classical and innovative analytical methods used in the analysis and detection of OTA in wine will be discussed together with an overview on the OTA occurrence in wine.

In: Food Science Research ... Volume 1
Editor: Lucille Monaco Cacioppo

ISBN: 978-1-63117-932-7
© 2014 Nova Science Publishers, Inc.

Chapter 92

WINE AND NEURODEGENERATIVE DISEASES

Pilar Zafrilla,[1,*] Juana Mulero,[1]
Adela Martínez-Cachá[1] and Emma Cantos[2]

[1]Departament Technology of Food and Nutrition
University Catholic San Antonio, Murcia, Spain
[2]IFAPA, Rancho de la Merced,. Trebujena,
Jerez de la Frontera (Cádiz), Spain

RESEARCH SUMMARY

Damage to DNA, lipids, and proteins by reactive oxygen species (oxidative free radicals) has been implicated in accelerated aging, degenerative diseases including cancer, Alzheimer's disease and Parkinson's disease, as well as cardiovascular disease. These diseases of old age are expected to increase significantly over the next few decades as people increasingly survive beyond the age of 80 years. Consequently there is interest in identifying lifestyle factors and molecular mechanisms that can minimize the risk of these debilitating conditions.

Quality of life is seriously compromised by cognitive impairment, dementia and Alzheimer's disease (AD).

Multiple epidemiological studies suggest that daily, moderate alcohol consumption and especially wine is associated with a lower incidence of dementia and a reduction in Alzheimer's disease.

In moderation and as part of an overall healthy diet, then wine does have health benefits, particularly red wine. Wine has been proven to reduce the risk of heart disease, some cancers and reduce the progression of disorders like Alzheimer's and Parkinson's Disease. Beware, Drink more than the recommended amount and your health benefits are lost and your health risks go up.

Consumption of up to three servings of wine daily is associated with a lower risk of AD in elderly individuals without the APOE epsilon-4 allele. It has been suggested that ethanol may directly stimulate the release of acetylcholine in the hippocampus, which is associated

---

* E-mail: mpzafrilla@pdi.ucam.edu.

with learning and memory. In a rat model, a moderate concentration of alcohol (0.8 g/kg) stimulated the release of acetylcholine while a higher concentration (2.4 g/kg) inhibited its release.

Red wine contains a complex mixture of bioactive compounds, including flavonols, monomeric and polymeric flavan-3-ols, highly colored anthocyanins, as well as phenolic acids and the stilbene polyphenol, resveratrol.

Resveratrol (found in grapes and wine which fights infection in vines) has demonstrated neuroprotective effects through its antioxidante and antiinflammatory capabilities, as well as its influence on activación of sirtuin 1 (SIRT1). Moreover evidence suggests the possibility that resveratrol can prevent neurodegeneration in Alzheimer`s disease via protección against beta-amyloid plaques and might also have the ability to decrease Huntington protein aggregates.

Researchers have found that resveratrol can help block the formation of amyloid plaques which are thought to damage brain cells and contribute to Alzheimer's disease.

Resveratrol, but not catechin or quercetin, decreased the level of intracellular amyloid-β produced by different cell lines expressing the wild type of Swedish mutant amyloid-β precursor protein (APP695) by promoting its intracellular degradation. This mechanism was proteasome-dependent, that is, resveratrol appeared to activate the proteasome involved in the degradation of amyloid-β, as the resveratrol-induced decrease of amyloid-β could be prevented by several selective proteasome inhibitors and by siRNA-directed silencing of the proteasome subunit $\beta 5$.

In this review we are going to analyze the effect of the wine in the neurodegenerative diseases, fundamentally in Alzheimer's disease and in Parkinson's disease.

In: Food Science Research ... Volume 1
Editor: Lucille Monaco Cacioppo

ISBN: 978-1-63117-932-7
© 2014 Nova Science Publishers, Inc.

Chapter 93

IMPACT OF WINEMAKING PROCESS IN MADEIRA WINE COMPOSITION: FROM AGING MARKERS TO ETHYL CARBAMATE (A CONTAMINANT)

Rosa Perestrelo,[1,2] *José S. Câmara*[2,3] *and Sílvia M. Rocha*[1,*]

[1]QOPNA, Departamento de Química, Universidade de Aveiro,
Aveiro, Portugal
[2]Centro de Química da Madeira, Campus Universitário da Penteada,
Funchal, Portugal
[3]Centro de Ciências Exactas e de Engenharia da Universidade da Madeira,
Campus Universitário da Penteada, Funchal, Portugal

RESEARCH SUMMARY

Madeira wine is a fortified Portuguese wine, which plays an important role in the economy of the Madeira Island. The peculiar characteristics of Madeira wines arise from the specific and singular winemaking and aging processes that promote many reactions, which are crucial to the final remarkable characteristics of the wine. However, it may also incur production of ethyl carbamate (EC). EC is potentially toxic, and was classified as a probable human carcinogen compound (Group 2A) by the International Agency for Research on Cancer. The establishment of potential age markers is of paramount significance as it may contribute to detect frauds and to ensure the authenticity of wine, whereas the study of toxic and carcinogenic substances (e.g. EC) represents one of the most demanding area in the food safety, due to their repercussions for public health. This chapter comprises an actual and detailed discussion about the age markers and EC in Madeira wine and their relation with the winemaking process. The recent achievements in this field arising from the application of GC × GC–ToFMS, a high throughput and sensitive methodology, are also discussed. Higher understanding and control of Madeira wine may be performed due to recent progresses in analytical methodologies.

---

* Corresponding author: E-mail address: smrocha@ua.pt (Sílvia M. Rocha). Tel. + 351 234401524; Fax. + 351 234370084.

In: Food Science Research ... Volume 1
Editor: Lucille Monaco Cacioppo

ISBN: 978-1-63117-932-7
© 2014 Nova Science Publishers, Inc.

Chapter 94

CONTROLLING THE HIGHS AND THE LOWS OF ALCOHOL IN WINE

Creina S. Stockley, Cristian Varela, Adrian Coulter,
Peter R. Dry, I. Leigh Francis,
Richard Muhlack and Isak S. Pretorius*
Australian Wine Research Institute, Glen Osmond,
Adelaide, Australia

RESEARCH SUMMARY

Amid a continuing 'hot' and intense public health debate about harmful alcohol consumption, taking control of the alcohol concentration in wine has become a priority for the wine sector worldwide. Despite a growing body of evidence indicating the health benefits of responsible, light to moderate wine consumption, and the generally healthy pattern of wine consumption (slowly with food), wine is still much criticised in these debates. Over the past two decades, worldwide the average alcohol concentration of wine has risen. In contrast, consumer studies show an increasing preference for lower-alcohol wines. Ironically, the alcohol component is actually responsible for much of the cardiovascular health benefits, for example. Producers and researchers are now develop-ping new ways to reduce alcohol in some wine styles. Getting the alcohol concentration and balance right with body and positive fruit flavours can be surprisingly difficult. Options include changes to viticultural practices (e.g. reducing leaf area); fermentation and winemaking practices (e.g. selecting low Brix grapes and use of yeast strains with lower fermentation efficiency); wine processing technologies (e.g. alcohol removal and increasing relative humidity for lengthy barrel maturation); as well as considering carefully consumer preferences when making high alcohol wines. The current challenge for the wine sector is how to manage best the 'dark side' of alcohol worldwide and the 'bright' side of wine and society.

---

* Correspondence to: Creina.Stockley@awri.com.au.

In: Food Science Research ... Volume 1
Editor: Lucille Monaco Cacioppo

ISBN: 978-1-63117-932-7
© 2014 Nova Science Publishers, Inc.

Chapter 95

INCREASING WINE QUALITY THROUGH THE USE OF OAK BARRELS: FACTORS THAT WILL INFLUENCE AGED WINE COLOR AND AROMA

P. Rodríguez-Rodríguez,
A. B. Bautista-Ortín and E. Gómez-Plaza[*]
Departamento de Tecnología de Alimentos, Nutrición y Bromatología,
Facultad de Veterinaria, Universidad de Murcia, Campus de Espinardo,
Murcia, Spain

RESEARCH SUMMARY

Aging wines in barrels improves their quality and contributes to their organoleptic characteristics. After a period of oak barrel maturation, the wines are enriched in aromatic substances, the color is more stable and mouthfeel complexity is improved.

This increased colour stability is due to the small amounts of air that penetrate through the wood pores and bunghole, a natural micro-oxygenation process that improves the polymerisation and condensation reactions among flavonoid compounds. These reactions directly affect the colour and astringency of wines, and modify their organo-leptic characteristics.

The complexity of the aroma is increased due to the extraction of certain compounds present in the wood, which are transferred to wine during the aging period, although reactions involving only wine compounds and the evaporation of volatile compounds may also occur during oak barrel maturing.

Factors which affect the extension of the reactions occurring during wine oak aging are the species and geographical origin of the wood, seasoning of the staves, toasting, the barrel volume and the age of the barrel. The role of each of these factors will be discussed.

On the negative side, barrels are expensive, take up a lot of space in the winery and their lifetime is not long. In addition, as the barrel becomes older, it might become populated with

---
[*] Corresponding author, e-mail: encarnag@um.es.

undesirable microorganisms such as Brettanomyces, which can produce sensorially significant concentrations of ethyl phenols with their unpleasant medicinal and horsy aromas. Alternatives have been developed to simplify the ageing process while ensuring that the wood-originated volatiles are released into the wine. One of these techniques consists of adding small pieces of wood, commonly known as oak chips, to the wine kept in stainless steel tanks or used barrels. This aging system will be also discussed.

In: Food Science Research ... Volume 1
Editor: Lucille Monaco Cacioppo

ISBN: 978-1-63117-932-7
© 2014 Nova Science Publishers, Inc.

Chapter 96

NON-*SACCHAROMYCES* YEASTS AND WINE

Pin-Rou Lee,[1] Xiao Li,[1] Bin Yu,[2] Philip Curran[2] and Shao-Quan Liu[1,]*

[1]Food Science and Technology Programme, Department of Chemistry,
National University of Singapore, Singapore
[2]Firmenich Asia Pte Ltd, Tuas, Singapore

RESEARCH SUMMARY

Wine fermentation is a complex bioprocess involving various microorganisms, especially yeasts and lactic acid bacteria, where yeasts play a prominent role. Of all the microorganisms involved, *Saccharomyces cerevisiae* yeast is the key player and is responsible for alcoholic fermentation and largely for flavour formation. It has been established that in spontaneous fermentation wine is not purely the result of biotransformation of grape musts by a single species or a single strain of yeasts and besides *Saccharomyces* yeasts, the indigenous, weakly fermentative non-*Saccharomyces* yeasts also impact on wine quality. Compared to the wines fermented with a single *Saccharomyces* yeast strain, spontaneous fermentation adds complexity of flavour and stylistic distinction.

The predominant species of non-*Saccharomyces* yeasts associated with spontaneous wine fermentation include those yeasts from the genera *Hanseniaspora, Candida, Kloeckera, Pichia, Zygosaccharomyces, Schizosaccharomyces, Torulaspora, Metschnikowia, Brettanomyes, Saccharomycodes* and *Williopsis*. Non-*Saccharomyces* yeasts were originally associated with production of off-flavour and wine spoilage. Nonetheless, non-*Saccharomyces* yeasts can produce secondary metabolites that positively contribute to the final organoleptic properties of wines (e.g. esters) as well as excrete enzymes (e.g. pectinases, glucanases and β-glucosidases) which can affect wine flavour upon bioconversion of non-volatile precursors into desirable aroma compounds such as oxygenated terpenes (citronellol, linalool, geraniol, etc.). *Saccharomyces* yeast is still essential to complete wine fermentation

* Contact: Food Science and Technology Programme, Department of Chemistry, National University of Singapore, 4 Science Drive 4, Singapore. Tel.: +65 6516 2687; fax: +65 6775 7895; E-mail address: chmLsq@nus.edu.sg (Shao-Quan Liu).

due to the low stress-tolerant ability of non-*Saccharomyces* yeasts. Fermentation of a mixed-culture of non-*Saccharomyces* and *Saccharomyces cerevisiae* yeasts takes advantage of the flavour-enhancing potential of the former and the ethanol-producing ability of the latter. Early death of non-*Saccharomyces* yeasts is an issue in mixed-culture fermentation due to several factors: competition for sugar uptake, space confinement, SO_2 concentration, oxygen availability, nutrient limitation, presence of toxic compounds, cell–cell contact and quorum sensing.

The potential of non-*Saccharomyces* yeasts in winemaking is still untapped. In order to exploit the potential benefits of non-*Saccharomyces* yeasts in wine fermentation and to minimize their negative impact on wine flavour (e.g. spoilage and off-flavour formation), more research should be conducted to better understand the biodiversity, physiology, metabolism, genetics, molecular pathways and cell biology of non-*Saccharomyces* yeasts.

In: Food Science Research ... Volume 1
Editor: Lucille Monaco Cacioppo

ISBN: 978-1-63117-932-7
© 2014 Nova Science Publishers, Inc.

Chapter 97

THE EFFECT OF BACTERIA QUALITY, THERMAL AND PHOTOCHEMICAL TREATMENT ON THE COMPOSITION OF VOLATILE ORGANIC COMPOUNDS IN WINE

Maurizio D'Auria and Rocco Racioppi

Dipartimento di Chimica "A. M. Tamburro", Università della Basilicata,
Potenza, Italy

RESEARCH SUMMARY

The effect of the variability of 36 *Saccharomyces Cerevisiae* wild strains on the composition of volatile organic compounds in the corresponding wines has been studied by using HS-SPME-CG-MS. This methodology has been used in order to determine the effect of both light and thermal treatments on the composition of volatile organic compounds on different wines.

In: Food Science Research ... Volume 1
Editor: Lucille Monaco Cacioppo

ISBN: 978-1-63117-932-7
© 2014 Nova Science Publishers, Inc.

Chapter 98

SENSORY AND ANTIOXIDANT EVALUATION OF SPARKLING WINES

Cláudia Alberici Stefenon,[1,2] *Camila de Martini Bonesi,*[2]
Daniel Prá,[3] *Carla Eliete Iochims dos Santos,*[3]
Johnny Ferraz Dias,[3] *João Antônio Pêgas Henriques,*[4]
Mirian Salvador[1] *and Regina Vanderlinde*[1]

[1]Instituto de Biotecnologia, Universidade de Caxias do Sul, Caxias do Sul, RS, Brasil;
[2]Laboratório Randon Ltda, Caxias do Sul, RS, Brasil
[3]Instituto de Física, Universidade Federal do Rio Grande do Sul, Porto Alegre, RS, Brasil
[4]Faculdade de Farmácia, Universidade Luterana do Brasil, Canoas, RS, Brasil

RESEARCH SUMMARY

The purpose of this study was to evaluate sensory properties, phenolic content, mineral profile and antioxidant activities of sparkling wines (SWs). Were studied fifteen SWs produced by seven different wineries located in the *Serra Gaúcha* (south of Brazil), divided into three equal groups (*Charmat brut*, *Charmat demi-sec* and *Champenoise*). The interactions among important characteristics of SWs are still not clarified, and biological activities as auxiliaries in health maintenance have become a goal of consumers around the world. *Charmat* and *Champenoise* methods have different interactions between mineral composition (mainly *demi-sec* samples) and phenolic profile in relationship to biological activity (all groups evaluated showed CAT-like and SOD-like antioxidant activities) and sensorial properties observed. These aspects play an important role in the maintenance of SWs quality and are essential to the sustainability of the wine industry. The results of the present study showed that SWs have bioactive compounds useful in a healthy diet, as manganese, rubidium and zinc. They further allow consumers to enjoy SWs of their choice without giving up any health benefits.

In: Food Science Research ... Volume 1
Editor: Lucille Monaco Cacioppo

ISBN: 978-1-63117-932-7
© 2014 Nova Science Publishers, Inc.

Chapter 99

THE POTENTIALITIES OF ULTRA-PERFORMANCE LIQUID CHROMATOGRAPHY COMBINED WITH PHOTODIODE ARRAY DETECTION IN THE ANALYSIS OF WINE METABOLITES WITH BIOACTIVE EFFECTS: THE CASE STUDY OF POLYPHENOLS

Jorge Pereira, Catarina Silva, João Gonçalves and José S. Câmara *

CQM/UMa - Centro de Química da Madeira, Centro de Ciências
Exactas e da Engenharia da Universidade da Madeira, Campus
Universitário da Penteada, Funchal, Portugal

RESEARCH SUMMARY

The volatile fraction of wine plays a prominent role in its organoleptic characteristics. It determines their aroma, which is the major contributor to overall flavour perception and one of the most important parameters influencing the wine quality and consumer acceptance. Their chemical composition contains numerous (over 1000 volatile compounds) small molecules belonging to distinct chemical families, including higher alcohols, ethyl esters, fatty acids, acetates, isoamyl esters, carbonyls, sulphurs, furan compounds, monoterpenoids, C_{13}-norisoprenoids and volatile phenols. Moreover, these compounds have different physicochemical properties regarding concentration (ranging from several mg L^{-1} (e.g., ethyl acetate) to less than a few ng L^{-1} (e.g., 3-isobutyl-2-methoxypyrazine, IBMP), polarity, volatility and odour impact. They are largely derived from four different sources: (*i*) the grape berry; (*ii*) processing of the grapes (namely crushing, pressing, etc) by chemical, enzymatic-chemical and thermal reaction in grape must; (*iii*) the yeast strain used for fermentation; and (*iv*) from containers used for wine making (wood, commonly oak) and chemical reactions during maturation wine storage.

* E-mail:jsc@uma.pt.

Fermentation alters the must by changing the conjugation of organic acids and phenolics, by extraction and formation of copigments and the development of an anaerobic and protective redox potential [1]. Therefore, wine composition is very heterogenic, involving around 80 % of water, 10-18 % alcohol, about 7 % of primary metabolites, namely sulphites, organic acids, sugars, proteins, vitamins and minerals and about 1 % of secondary metabolites biologically active, the most important of which are polyphenols. And although the least representative in terms of abundance in wine composition, these metabolites have a strong influence on the quality and character of the wine, being responsible for their organoleptic properties, such as colour (anthocyanins or curcumin, for example), astringency (tannins), bitterness (flavanols), taste, oxidation level, clarity and activity of important bacteria in the vinification and wine aging processes [2, 3]. Moreover, there are thousands of recent reports presenting evidences of the bioactive effects of polyphenols from different origins, including wine, which are probably responsible for the "French paradox" observation. This expression, used for the first time in 1819 by the Irish physician Samuel Black, describes precisely the low incidence of coronary heart disease in France, despite they have a diet relatively rich in saturated fats, something that is not observed in other countries like USA or Canada with no tradition on the consumption of red wine [4].

Polyphenols constitute one of the most common and widespread groups of substances in flowering plants, occurring in all vegetative organs, as well as in flowers and fruits. They are considered plant secondary metabolites, arising biogenetically from either the shikimate /phenylpropanoid pathway or 'polyketide' acetate/malonate pathway, or both, and are generally involved in defence against ultraviolet radiation and in the chemical defence of plants against predators and in plant-plant interferences. To date, several hundreds of different polyphenols have been described and the number continues to increase [5]. According to the definition proposed by the investigators White, Bate-Smith, Swain and Haslam (WBSSH, pioneers in the vegetable tannins studies) polyphenols are water-soluble phenolic compounds having molecular masses up to 4 kDa and possessing 12 to 16 phenolic hydroxyl groups and 5 to 7 aromatic rings per 1 kDa (6). However, nowadays this definition is much broader, encompassing a wide variety of molecules that contain at least one aromatic ring with one or more hydroxyl groups in addition to other substituents (Figure 1). In a systematic way, we can classify polyphenols according with the number of phenolic rings they contain and the structural elements and substituents that bind these rings to one another [7]. In this way, polyphenols can be divided in flavonoids and non-flavonoids, being the compounds of first class the most abundant. Flavonoids share a common basic structure with two aromatic rings bounded together by three carbon atoms that form an oxygenated heterocycle [8]. The modifications of the central C-ring will originate several subclasses, namely flavonols, flavones, isoflavones, flavanones, catechins, anthocyanidins and procyanidins. The non-flavonoid polyphenols include the simplest phenolic acids, which are derivatives of benzoic and hydroxycinnamic acids, stilbenes, from which resveratrol is the most prominent representative, and lignans. Phenolic acids account for about a third of the polyphenolic compounds in our diet and are found in all plant material, but are particularly abundant in acidic-tasting fruits. Caffeic acid, gallic acid, ferulic acid are some common phenolic acids.

In: Food Science Research ... Volume 1
Editor: Lucille Monaco Cacioppo

ISBN: 978-1-63117-932-7
© 2014 Nova Science Publishers, Inc.

Chapter 100

WINE PHENOLICS: CHEMISTRY, BIOSYNTHESIS AND EFFECTS ON HEALTH

Hasim Kelebek[1] and Serkan Selli[2]
[1]University of Adiyaman, Adiyaman Vocational School,
Department of Food Technology, Adiyaman, Turkey
[2]University of Cukurova, Faculty of Agriculture,
Department of Food Engineering, Adana, Turkey

RESEARCH SUMMARY

Wine contains many phenolic components, most of which originate in the grape cultivars. They contribute to sensory characteristics such as color, flavor, astringency and hardness of wine directly or by interaction with proteins, polysaccharides, or other phenolic compounds. The main phenolic compounds deriving from grape can be divided in two groups, non-flavonoid and flavonoid (anthocyanins, flavan-3-ols and flavonols) compounds. The non-flavonoid phenolic constituents present in wine are mainly hydroxybenzoic and hydroxycinnamic acids as well as volatile phenols, stilbenes. Moreover, even if those compounds are colorless or slightly yellow, they have an important role in red wine color since they are known to enhance and stabilize the color of red wines by intra- and intermolecular reactions. They furthermore contribute to wine flavor and some of them also exhibit potent biological activities. Anthocyanins are the main pigments responsible for the color of the grapes and young red wines. They are localized in the solid parts of cluster and are extracted by maceration in the fermenting must. Flavan-3-ols (monomeric catechin and proanthocyanidins) are another large family of polyphenolic compounds in wines, which are mainly responsible for the structure of wines such as astringency and bitterness. The last groups of flavonoids present in wines are the flavonols such as quercetin, myricetin, kaempferol, isorhamnetin and their glycosides.

The biosynthesis of the phenolic compounds begins with the aromatic amino acid phenylalanine, a product of the shikimate pathway. Red wines have a higher content of total phenolics and contain a wider spectrum of phenolics than the white wines. The total content of phenolics in wine depends on a number of factors such as types of grapes (red or white) used for vinification and their extraction (temperature and maceration time), procedures employed for wine making and chemical reactions that occur during the aging of wine. A complex relationship exists between the factors that influence wine quality.

A large number of epidemiological and experimental studies have shown that the moderate consumption of wine, particularly red wine, helps to prevent coronary heart disease and some types of cancers. Wines, especially red wines, contain a large variety of antioxidants including resveratrol, catechin, epicatechin and proanthocyanidins. Of all the components of wine, especially resveratrol, which is a natural component specifically present in wine, has been identified as being mainly responsible for these health-promoting properties.

This present chapter explains the chemistry, occurrence and health properties of wine phenolic compounds.

In: Food Science Research … Volume 1
Editor: Lucille Monaco Cacioppo

ISBN: 978-1-63117-932-7
© 2014 Nova Science Publishers, Inc.

Chapter 101

DIFFERENCES IN *PINOT NOIR* RED WINES PRODUCED BY DIFFERENT METHODS: CHROMATOGRAPHIC, SPECTROSCOPIC, AND ELECTRO AIDED STUDY

Heli Sirén[1], Kimmo Sirén[2], Sandeep Sharma[1],
Laura Kaijanen[1], Jaana Ruokonen[1],
Mélanie Bricka[3] and Stella Rovio[4]

[1]Lappeenranta University of Technology, Lappeenranta, Finland
[2]Wine Consulting Kimmo Sirén, Lönnrotinkatu, Helsinki, Finland
[3]Chemical Engineering Department, Université Claude Bernard Lyon I, Lyon, France,
[4]VTT, Espoo, Finland

RESEARCH SUMMARY

The aim of the research was to study composition of Pinot Noir wines from U.S.A., France, New Zealand, and Chile. Pinot Noir grapes are difficult to grow and therefore differences were expected between products made by natural and artificial methods.

The study is divided into two parts. Firstly, the published literatures reviewed by endogenous and exogenous compounds in red wines by separation techniques and elemental analyses. Secondly, the article contains a report on the sensory evaluation and the experimental work done for specifying the differences in eight Pinot Noir red wines from different wine production countries. The wines were studied in detail to identify compounds that are produced during the production processes. The compounds were carbohydrates, carboxylic acids, and other native compounds that originate from grapes. In addition, the task was to specify some of the compounds that migrated into the products due to farming. Both chemical analyses and the sensory evaluation revealed clear differences among the wine samples.

In: Food Science Research ... Volume 1
Editor: Lucille Monaco Cacioppo

ISBN: 978-1-63117-932-7
© 2014 Nova Science Publishers, Inc.

Chapter 102

MICROBIAL CONTAMINATION AND SPOILAGE OF CONSUMER MILK – FACTS AND FICTION

*Valerie De Jonghe[1], An Coorevits[2,3], Sophie Marchand[1],
Anita Van Landschoot[2], Jan De Block[1], Els Van Coillie[1],
Paul De Vos[3] and Marc Heyndrickx[1,4]*

[1]Institute for Agricultural and Fisheries Research (ILVO), Technology and
Food Science Unit, Brusselsesteenweg, Melle, Belgium
[2]Laboratory of Biochemistry and Brewing, Faculty of Applied Engineering Sciences,
University College Ghent, Campus Schoonmeersen, Schoonmeersstraat,
Ghent, Belgium
[3]Laboratory of Microbiology (LM-UGent), Department of Biochemistry and
Microbiology, Faculty of Sciences, Ghent University,
K.L. Ledeganckstraat, Ghent, Belgium
[4]Department of Pathology, Bacteriology and Poultry Diseases, Faculty of Veterinary
Sciences, Ghent University, Salisburylaan, Merelbeke

RESEARCH SUMMARY

Bacterial spoilage of milk and dairy products causes great economical losses for the dairy industry. This chapter reviews current knowledge on the most important spoilage organisms and enzymes of microbial origin and their importance throughout the dairy chain in light of commercially applied processing conditions. The organoleptic and texture effects of spoilage enzymes on milk and dairy products are also discussed.

Aerobe spore-formers belonging to the genus *Bacillus sensu lato* and psychrotolerant Gram-negative rods belonging to the genus *Pseudomonas* are considered the most important spoilage micro-organisms in dairy products. Furthermore, the former do not only affect the quality of dairy products but are also occasionally implicated in food intoxications.

Operational management throughout the dairy chain can influence species composition and bacterial load of raw milk prior to processing. At the farm, variable feeding and housing strategies of cows, as well as seasonal differences, can influence the microbial quality of milk. Furthermore, psychrotolerant bacteria, such as the pseudomonads, will benefit from prolonged cold storage throughout the dairy chain.

Though these spoilage organisms have been subject of many studies and are thus historically well-known, recent large-scale raw milk isolation campaigns with identification based on current taxonomic insights and coupled to an extensive screening for enzymatic properties, support the need for re-evaluating the dominant species concerning dairy spoilage within these two groups of organisms (*Bacillus s.l.* and the genus *Pseudomonas*).

In: Food Science Research ... Volume 1
Editor: Lucille Monaco Cacioppo

ISBN: 978-1-63117-932-7
© 2014 Nova Science Publishers, Inc.

Chapter 103

APPLICABILITY OF PULSED FIELD GEL ELECTROPHORESIS FOR THE IDENTIFICATION OF LIPOLYTIC AND/OR PROTEOLYTIC PSYCHROTROPHIC *PSEUDOMONAS* SPECIES IN RAW MILK

P. D. Button[1,2,4], H. Roginski[2,5], H. C. Deeth[3] and H. M. Craven[1]

[1]CSIRO Food and Nutritional Sciences,
Werribee, Victoria, Australia
[2]School of Agriculture and Food Systems,
The University of Melbourne, Gilbert Chandler campus, Werribee, Victoria, Australia
[3]School of Agriculture and Food Sciences, The University of Queensland, St. Lucia,
Queensland, Australia
[4] School of Applied Sciences, RMIT University, Melbourne, Victoria, Australia
[5]Department of Agriculture and Food Systems, The University of Melbourne,
Parkville Campus, Victoria, Australia

RESEARCH SUMMARY

Many types of microorganisms are present in the milk collection environment and diversity in the raw milk microflora is typical, without dominance of a single species. The proportion of psychrotrophic bacteria in raw milk can vary widely and is associated with the level of farm hygiene. Studies in Europe have shown that typically, no more than 10% of the flora of good quality milk will be psychrotrophic with *Pseudomonas* species comprising a substantial proportion of these. *Pseudomonas fluorescens*, the most common species of the genus present in raw milk, has been involved in bacterial spikes (sudden elevations in total bacterial count) in farm bulk tank milk. Psychrotrophic *Pseudomonas* species play an important role in spoilage of UHT milk through the production of heat-stable lipases and proteases in raw milk that retain activity following UHT processing. Lipase and protease, produced by psychrotrophic *Pseudomonas* species are detected when the cell count exceeds

~10^6 cfu/mL. Prolonged refrigerated (4 °C) storage of raw milk increases the proportion of *Pseudomonas* species as do slightly higher temperatures (for example 6 °C) over a shorter period of time. This in turn increases the likelihood that they will produce heat-stable lipases and proteases. Furthermore, temperature fluctuations have been shown historically to occur in farm bulk milk, and the temperature of raw milk at the time of collection can vary widely. While less likely to occur today, both these scenarios could further compound the problem of *Pseudomonas* species proliferation in raw milk.

The aim of the present study was to investigate the use of pulsed field gel electrophoresis (PFGE) for identifying sources of lipase and/or protease producing psychrotrophic *Pseudomonas* species at various pre-processing locations, and to track the types identified through the pre-processing environment. Incubation of raw milk was also carried out to simulate possible scenarios where the raw milk may be stored on the farm and in the silo prior to UHT processing. This enabled enrichment for spoilage bacteria and studies to identify sources of microorganisms that may contribute to lipolysis and proteolysis in raw and, subsequently, UHT milk or other long life dairy products. The impact of various storage conditions on the different Pulsed Field (PF) types of importance with regard to lipase and protease production was also assessed.

In: Food Science Research … Volume 1
Editor: Lucille Monaco Cacioppo

ISBN: 978-1-63117-932-7
© 2014 Nova Science Publishers, Inc.

Chapter 104

RAW SHEEP MILK IN THE PROVINCE OF KARAK: PRODUCTION, CONSUMPTION AND HEALTH EFFECTS

Riadh AL-Tahiri

Department of Nutrition and Food Science, Faculty of Agriculture
University of Mutah, Karak, Jordan

RESEARCH SUMMARY

Sheep milk characterized by its high percentage of fat (6-8%) and high protein percentage (4.2-4.8), besides it has a very pronounce organoleptic characteristics which make it ideal to produce dairy products with a very special taste and with long shelf-life (ghee, Jameed and Baladi cheese).

This article showed that a deficient milk refrigeration system in the small farm, beside the lack of sanitation during milking and handling constitute major factors in milk deterioration. Pasteurization of Baladi cheese milk and the boiling process of Baladi cheese have a great effort on improving the microbiological quality and the sensory evaluation of the final product.

In: Food Science Research ... Volume 1
Editor: Lucille Monaco Cacioppo

ISBN: 978-1-63117-932-7
© 2014 Nova Science Publishers, Inc.

Chapter 105

RAW MILK: PRODUCTION, CONSUMPTION AND HEALTH BENEFITS

Marcelo A. Ferraz[1], Claudio Antonio Versiani Paiva[2], Marcelo R. Souza[3] and Mônica M. O. P. Cerqueira[3]

[1] Food Engineering, M.Sc. Animal Science, Brazil
[2] Secretary of Agriculture/Federal District, Brazil
[3] Professor at Veterinary School/Universidade Federal de Minas Gerais state, Brazil

RESEARCH SUMMARY

The milk production has been growing around the world, but the biggest growth is in South and North America (Brazil and USA) and Asia (India and China). World cow's milk production in 2008 stood at over 578 million tones, with the top ten producing countries representing about 55.4% of production. Countries with advantage on land and animal feed will be a differential of productivity, such as India, China and Brazil. The consumption has grown following the increase in population and income. The countries from North America and Oceania are the biggest consumer, but don't consume the needs, which is about 200 liters per capita per year (WHO). The lowest consume is observed in countries from Asia and Africa, but just in this countries are observed the biggest growth in income. The quantity of milk's ingestion must be considered, since the vitamins and supplements are necessary to bones, muscles and immune system. Health benefits of milk included good bone health, robust skin, good immune system, prevention of illnesses such as hypertension, dental decay, dehydration, respiratory problems, obesity, osteoporosis and even some forms of cancer. The beneficial health nutrients obtained from milk are mandatory for human body and help in prevention of chronic ailments. Keeping away severe illnesses and harmful factors can be done through increasing milk consumption.

In: Food Science Research ... Volume 1
Editor: Lucille Monaco Cacioppo

ISBN: 978-1-63117-932-7
© 2014 Nova Science Publishers, Inc.

Chapter 106

CAMEL MILK AS THERAPEUTIC ALTERNATIVE TO TREAT DIABETES; COMPARISON WITH INSULIN

Amel Sboui[1,2]*, Touhami Khorchani[1], Mongi Djegham[3] and Omrane Belhadj[2]

[1]Laboratoire d'Elevage et de la Faune Sauvage,
Institut des Régions Arides, Médenine Tunisie
[2]Laboratoire de Biochimie et Techno Biologie,
Faculté des Sciences de Tunis, Tunisie
[3]Laboratoire de Physiologie thérapeutique,
Ecole Nationale de Médecine Vétérinaire Sidi Thabet Tunisie

RESEARCH SUMMARY

This study was performed to evaluate the efficacy of camel milk on alloxan-induced diabetic dogs and to follow this effect in addition to Can-insulin®.

Four groups, composed of 4 diabetic dogs each, were used as follow: group 1 was getting camel milk, and group 2 treated simultaneous with camel milk and Can-insulin®, and group 3 received cow milk simultaneous with Can-insulin®. Group 4 contained clinically healthy animals and was used as control. Each dog received 500 ml of milk/day during five weeks.

After three weeks, group 1 showed a significant decline on blood glucose levels from 10.33 ± 0.55 to 6.22 ± 0.5 mmol/L, this improvement on glycemic control was accompanied to a significant decrease on total proteins concentrations (from 79.66 ± 2.11 to 63.63 ± 4.43 g/L). A significant decline of cholesterol levels (from 6.84 ± 1.2 to 4.9 ± 0.5 mmol/L) was shown after only two weeks of treatment. The same result was illustrated on group 2 treated simultaneous with camel milk and Can-Insulin. In group 3 the effect of Can-insulin was well shown only on blood glucose levels during the treatment.

The investigation in this research was the beneficial effect of camel milk on diabetic dogs and its independence to the treatment with Can-insulin®.

* Corresponding author: Amel SBOUI E-mail: amelsb6@yahoo.fr Address: Arid Land Institute, Livestock and Wildlife Laboratory Route Edjorf, Elfgè 4119, Medenine, Tunisia, Phone number: +216.75.633.005, Fax number: +216.75.633.006

In: Food Science Research ... Volume 1
Editor: Lucille Monaco Cacioppo

ISBN: 978-1-63117-932-7
© 2014 Nova Science Publishers, Inc.

Chapter 107

PROGRESS IN PASTEURIZATION PROCESSING OF RAW MILK: BACTERICIDAL EFFECT AND EXTENSION OF SHELF LIFE, IMPACTS ON THE PHYSICOCHEMICAL PROPERTIES, MILK COMPONENTS, FLAVOR AND PROCESSING CHARACTERISTICS

Ruijin Yang, Sha Zhang and Wei Zhao

State Key Laboratory of Food Science and Technology & School of Food Science and Technology, Jiangnan University, Wuxi, Jiangsu, China

RESEARCH SUMMARY

Milk is a type of nutritionally complete food which contains protein, fat, lactose, vitamins, and minerals. The high nutritional content value of milk has become an excellent broth for a variety of microorganisms, which include many sorts of pathogens, such as (*Escherichia. coli, Listeria), (monocytogenes* and *Bacillus cereus*); (Fox and Cameron, 1982). The main purpose of pasteurization is to exterminate such pathogens in order to ensure the safety of milk and extend its shelf life. However, the pasteurization could also influence the physicochemical properties of milk, such as the changes of nutrient component which may reduce the digestibility and nutritional value of milk. Meantime, the sensory quality of milk also decreased slightly due to the heat treatment.

In: Food Science Research ... Volume 1
Editor: Lucille Monaco Cacioppo

ISBN: 978-1-63117-932-7
© 2014 Nova Science Publishers, Inc.

Chapter 108

CONTROLLED ATMOSPHERE-BASED IMPROVED STORAGE OF COLD RAW MILK: POTENTIAL OF N_2 GAS

Patricia Munsch-Alatossava and *Tapani Alatossava*

Department of Food and Environmental Sciences,
Division of Food Technology,
FIN-00014 University of Helsinki, Finland

RESEARCH SUMMARY

On one hand, according to FAO about 80% of the milk consumed worldwide is mostly obtained out of standards; in developed countries on the other hand an effective cold chain selects for spoiling bacteria that inflict significant losses to the dairy industry. Most studies, that concern modified or controlled atmospheres applied to bovine raw milk, were mostly based on CO_2 treatments, or for a few on mixtures of CO_2 and N_2 gases; a commonly accepted thought is that antimicrobial effects are associated with the application of CO_2, whereas N_2 has been employed as an inert gas component. Some recent studies, performed with an open system, based on a constant flushing of N_2 gas through the headspace of a vessel, at laboratory or at pilot scale suggest that bacterial growth could be substantially reduced by flushing pure N_2 gas alone into raw milk, with significant effects on mesophilic and psychrotrophic aerobes, but also on some other bacterial groups, without favouring the growth of anaerobes. One major observation was that phospholipases producers among them *Bacillus cereus* could be excluded at laboratory scale by the N_2 gas-based flushing; the inhibitory effect was also noticeable to some extend at pilot scale. Possible antimicrobial mechanisms underlying the use of N_2 gas, as well as the potential of controlled atmospheres-based treatments of raw milk will be discussed.

---

* Emails: patricia.munsch@helsinki.fi; tapani.alatossava@helsinki.fi